herbs & spices
of Thailand

Marshall Cavendish
Editions

Reprinted 2010

Recipes and accompanying photographs, including photographs on page 9,
from *Feast of Flavours from the Thai Kitchen* published by Marshall Cavendish Cuisine

Published by Marshall Cavendish Editions
An imprint of Marshall Cavendish International
1 New Industrial Road, Singapore 536196

Other Marshall Cavendish Offices:
Marshall Cavendish International. PO Box 65829, London EC1P 1NY, UK • Marshall
Cavendish Corporation. 99 White Plains Road, Tarrytown NY 10591-9001, USA • Marshall
Cavendish International (Thailand) Co Ltd. 253 Asoke, 12th Flr, Sukhumvit 21 Road,
Klongtoey Nua, Wattana, Bangkok 10110, Thailand • Marshall Cavendish (Malaysia) Sdn
Bhd, Times Subang, Lot 46, Subang Hi-Tech Industrial Park, Batu Tiga, 40000 Shah Alam,
Selangor Darul Ehsan, Malaysia

National Library Board (Singapore) Cataloguing in Publication Data
Tan, Hugh T. W.
Herbs & spices of Thailand / Hugh T.W. Tan. – Singapore :
Times Editions-Marshall Cavendish, c2005.
p. cm.
Includes bibliographical references and index.
ISBN-13 : 978-981-232-968-4
1. Herbs – Thailand. 2. Spices – Thailand. 3. Cookery, Thai. I. Title.
TX406
641.357 — dc21   SLS2005027238

Printed in Singapore by KWF Printing Co.

herbs & spices
of Thailand

contents

Many would agree that Thai cuisine is one of the best in the world, if not the best. Made with fresh ingredients, Thai food is aromatic, tasty, healthy and full of interesting textures. Its aromas and tastes are largely a result of the unique herbs and spices used. Surprisingly, it is not the number of herbs and spices used but the intelligent combination or blending of tastes that makes Thai food so distinctive and wonderful.

The Southeast Asian nation of Thailand stretches 1,640 km from north to south and 880 km from east to west, with an area of 514,000 sq km. Known as Siam until 1939, it is formally called the Kingdom of Thailand today. Thailand shares borders with Myanmar (formerly Burma) in the west and northwest, Laos in the north and northeast, Cambodia in the east and Peninsular Malaysia in the south. Throughout its history, Thailand has been enriched by many diverse peoples, resulting in an interesting ethnic and religious mix, especially at the border regions. Today's population of about 65 million consists mainly of Thai (75%), Chinese (14%) and other ethnic groups, mainly hill tribe peoples. Most are Buddhists (95%), followed by Muslims (3.8%), Christians (0.5%), Hindus (0.1%) and other religious groups. It is hardly surprising that, given the nation's geographical location and history, Thai cuisine has evolved to reflect these different cultures and ethnicities.

The northern half of Thailand has a tropical monsoon climate, with rainy, warm and cloudy weather during the southwest monsoon (mid-May to September) and dry and cooler weather during the northeast monsoon (November to mid-March). The southern half of Thailand (the isthmus), however, has a tropical climate which is always hot and humid. Southern Thais often joke that they have three seasons each year — hot, hotter and hottest! The monsoonal or tropical climate and diverse altitudinal ranges allow a wide variety of tropical and subtropical herbs and spices to grow.

Thailand's terrain consists of a central plain, with the Khorat Plateau in the east, while the rest of the country is mountainous, rising up to 2,576 m at the summit of Doi Inthanon. The central plain is not only geographically central, it is also agriculturally vital because this is where extensive rice cultivation occurs. Rice is the main source of carbohydrate in a typical Thai meal and a wonderful complement to signature spicy dishes — like a white canvas that contrasts wonderfully with bold coloured brushstrokes in a beautiful painting.

The 32 herbs and spices presented here are found in most of the dishes in Thai cooking. Each herb or spice will be described in detail to include its scientific and common names; its unique plant structure and varied uses; tips on storage; common Thai dishes in which it is used; as well as additional notes of interest. This book will be useful to the Thai food enthusiast who might want to know more about the definitive ingredients of Thai cuisine; to the novice cook who might want to know more about these herbs and spices; and finally, to those who might want to discover more about the plants themselves.

Thai Cuisine >>>

In a very small nutshell, Thai cuisine is a hybrid or fusion cuisine, which has influences from Chinese soup and noodle dishes to Indian curries and Indonesian and Malaysian *satay* (spicy, barbecued and skewered meats) — a reflection of its political history, trade and geography. Yet Thai cuisine retains its own unique identity, like the Thai people who are fiercely proud of their culture and traditions.

Each dish strives for harmony and usually incorporates the contrasting flavours of sweet-ness, sourness, saltiness and spicy hotness (or pungency). The latter refers to the spicy hotness of chillies for which there is no exact English translation, since "hot" refers to heat (a physical property) rather than spiciness (a chemical property). The closest English word to this meaning is perhaps "pungent", which dictionaries define as causing a sharp and irritating sensation. The Thai word *phet* and the Malay word *pedas* more accurately reflect this condition. Not all Thai food is spicy-hot, so there are plenty of dishes which will suit the tamer Western palate.

Thai meals, like those in other Southeast Asian countries, do not come in sequential courses. A meal centres on rice, which is the main source of carbohydrate. Rice is practically tasteless, so it nicely complements the flavourful dishes that are served with it. Southern Thais prefer eating long-grained, padi-grown rice while northern Thais are partial to the short-grained or sticky glutinous rice grown in dry ground in the hills. The side dishes in Thai cuisine may consist of curries, which are more for flavouring the rice. In general, little beef, pork or chicken is used because meat is relatively expensive. And because most of the chopping and slicing is done prior to cooking (as in Chinese cuisine), Thais only use what North Americans and Europeans call a dessert fork and spoon at meal times; the knife is generally unnecessary.

Fish is the major source of protein in Thai cuisine, largely because Thailand has a long coastline and numerous rivers and canals that make fishing a key industry. Fish is also cheap since most are captured from the sea or freshwater canals and even in padi fields while some are reared in ponds. Even the main flavouring ingredients usually have seafood in them, such as the strongly flavoured and extremely salty fish sauce (*nahm pla*) and the pungently aromatic prawn paste (*kapee*), both of which are used in practically all Thai dishes. The other distinctly Thai flavours come from the herbs and spices as well as other plant products, including basil, chillies, coconut milk, coriander, cumin, galangal, ginger, lemon grass, lime juice, palm sugar, pepper, shallots, spring onions, tamarind, turmeric and others. Chillies arrived in Thailand in the early 16th century, brought by Portuguese traders, and have become so central to Thai food that we now associate fiery hot or *phet* food to be authentically Thai. The tangy flavour is provided by lime juice, lemon grass and tamarind juice.

Thai food, like Chinese food, is often stir-fried or steamed in a wok. With stir-frying, the ingredients are flash-fried and sometimes cooked even as it is brought to the table to be served! This way, the goodness and vitamins of the ingredients are not destroyed and the dishes make for a healthier or more nutritious meal. Steamed ingredients must also be very fresh, especially meats or seafood, and this is another hallmark of Thai food — the fresh ingredients that are used, such as liberal amounts of raw vegetables as well as herbs and spices to garnish each dish.

What are Herbs & Spices? >>>

Herbs

and spices are essentially plant products or their mixtures that are used to flavour or season food. Herbs are plants with little or no woody tissue (they are soft-stemmed), the upper portions of which are used fresh or dried to season food. Spices include all other aromatic dried plant products — including arils, barks, flower buds, fruits, leaves, rhizomes and other parts of woody plants such as trees, shrubs and climbers — that are used, likewise, to season food. Herbs are usually associated with temperate flavouring plants, spices with tropical and subtropical ones. This distinction between herb and spice is debatable and there are instances whereby a herb or spice may be referred to incorrectly. For example, in commerce, the seed of coriander, a herbaceous plant, is called a spice seed when, in fact, it is a herb seed. In this book, all the spices belong to flowering plants or angiosperms, which are characterised by the possession of a special reproductive structure (the flower) and what develops from it (the fruit). In fact, for some of the flavouring plants in this book, the source of the seasoning comes from the flowers or their associated parts.

How to Use this Book >>>

Each herb or spice will be described as follows:

1. **Scientific or botanical name of the species**

    All species of biological organisms (animal, bacterium, fungus, plant or protist) have a scientific name. This tends to be much more accurate as naming is usually applied with scientific rigour. Common names, on the other hand, may be coined in any fashion and may also apply to more than one plant, making the name a homonym.

2. **Synonym (or synonyms) of the scientific or botanical name of the species**

    This is useful to know in that when we refer to older literature, we will be able to identify the species. The application of a scientific name to a particular species can also vary from author to author so providing the synonym helps us decipher the reference.

3. **Scientific or botanical name of the family of the species**

    All plants belong to a larger family of plants. Plants in the same family are more closely related and have various features in common, ranging from their general shape or form, the form of their individual parts, their biochemistry, physiology and other characteristics.

4. **Common names in English and romanised Thai**

    The common or vernacular name is the name of the species used in everyday language. Not all plants have common names as some are so rare that only scientists have come across them.

5. **Common family name of the species**

    The common or vernacular name is the name of the family used in everyday language.

6. **Botanical description of the plant**

    Highlighted here are the part or parts used to flavour food, including the chemical or chemicals which produce the flavours.

7. **Storage of the herb or spice**

    Described here are simple and efficient methods for storing the herbs and spices so as to increase their shelf life.

8. **Common Thai dishes in which the species is used**

    Given the multitude of dishes available, I have listed only the more popular dishes.

9. **Additional notes of interest**

The herbs or spices are arranged alphabetically by their scientific or botanical names, for the simple reason that plants can have many common or vernacular names, whereas most have only one scientific or botanical name. The common names are also listed in the index. Occasionally, plants have been scientifically named twice or more. In such cases the synonym or synonyms which also apply to this species are listed.

For technical terms that are not explained in the text, the glossary at the back of the book provides their meanings.

All the plant parts on these two pages are featured to scale in relation to the 1-baht coin which is 2 cm in diameter.

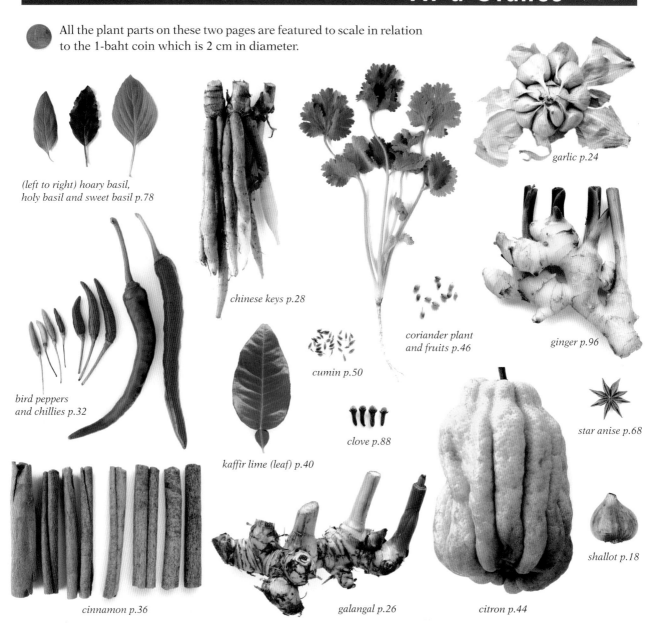

(left to right) hoary basil, holy basil and sweet basil p.78

chinese keys p.28

coriander plant and fruits p.46

garlic p.24

ginger p.96

bird peppers and chillies p.32

cumin p.50

clove p.88

kaffir lime (leaf) p.40

star anise p.68

shallot p.18

cinnamon p.36

galangal p.26

citron p.44

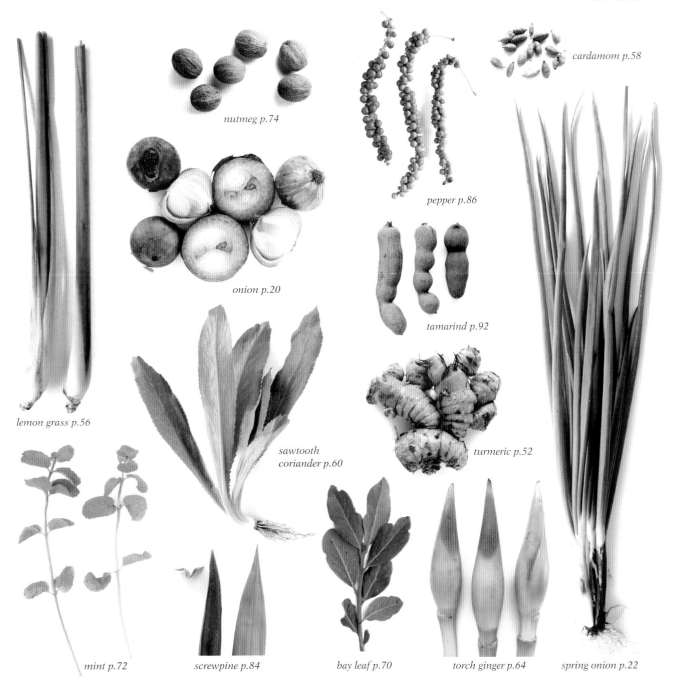

nutmeg p.74

cardamom p.58

onion p.20

pepper p.86

tamarind p.92

lemon grass p.56

sawtooth
coriander p.60

turmeric p.52

mint p.72

screwpine p.84

bay leaf p.70

torch ginger p.64

spring onion p.22

Herbs & Spices >>>

longitudinal section

cross-section

top view

side view

bottom view

bag of shallots as sold in markets

Shallot

Scientific or botanical name:
Allium cepa cultivar group *Aggregatum*

Synonyms:
Allium cepa var. *ascalonicum*,
Allium cepa var. *aggregatum*,
Allium cepa var. *solanina*

Scientific or botanical name of family:
Liliaceae

Common names:
English: shallot, potato onion, multiplier onion
Thai: *hom*, *hom-daeng*, *hom-lek*

Common family name:
lily family

Botanical Description:
This plant consists of a bunch of bulbs which grow together. Each pear-shaped bulb consists of a flattened conical stem at its base, bearing fleshy, concentrically overlapping leaves which narrow at the tip of the bulb. There are three to eight cylindrical, hollow leaves which grow in two rows, extending as a sheath from the base of the bulb. The distal portions of the leaves are light to dark green and have a waxy bloom. The height from the bottom of the bulb to the tips of the leaves may reach 50 cm. Fibrous roots arise from the base of each bulb. The flowering shoot, or scape, arises from the bottom of the bulb and is usually taller than the rest of the plant. It consists of a single stalk that becomes hollow at maturity, bearing at the tip a circular bunch of some 50 to 2,000 greenish white flowers. The flower stalks all arise from a central point (known as an umbel). After fertilisation, each flower forms a fruit which splits open to release tiny, black, wrinkled seeds. Each fruit may yield up to six seeds.

This plant is a biennial, meaning the seed will grow into a plant which stores its food in the bulb in the first year, then die down only to grow again, producing flowers, fruits and seeds, by using the food reserves in the bulb in the second year. The seeds allow it to reproduce again. Human utilisation, however, exploits this plant as an annual by planting the bulbs to produce more bulbs (asexually), which are then harvested before they produce flowers.

Uses:

The raw bulb of the plant is used as food, seasoning and spice because of its pungency. When used as a spice for meats and seafood, shallots may be sliced and mixed with soy sauce or ground and blended with other ingredients. It is also pickled or fried. The young inflorescence (flowering shoot) can be eaten as a vegetable. Used throughout the world's cuisines, cultivated *Allium* plants are probably the most indispensable ingredient.

The pungency in shallots is dependant on the amount of S-alk(en)nyl cysteine sulphoxides per unit in fresh weight.

Because of its antibacterial properties, shallots are also used in traditional medicine for reducing fevers or healing wounds. Farmers in some areas grow garlic and shallots in plots which were previously used to grow other crops to 'cleanse' the plots of pathogens as part of crop rotation practice. The plant can also be used to lower blood sugar levels and inhibit platelet aggregation when eaten raw or cooked or consumed as an extract or powder.

Storage:

Shallots are sold with the outer covering dried and can be stored for months in a cool, dry place. The dried outer layers (dried fleshy leaf bases) are removed before use.

In Thai Dishes:

Slice the shallots crosswise and separate them into rings or slice lengthwise to have the slices intact. The crosswise segments are often fried till golden brown, and these impart a very flavourful aroma. Fried shallots are used as a garnish in salads and soups. Shallots are essential ingredients in Thai sauces and pastes; especially popular is the basic dipping sauce *nahm phrik paw* where the basic ingredients are roasted to accentuate the blend of spices. The pungency of fresh shallots also gives a nice edge to salads, and here they are sliced lengthwise so that the segments remain intact.

Salads

laab gai (northeastern chicken salad with
mint and lemon grass)
laab neua (northeastern beef salad with
mint and lemon grass)
yam pla muk (squid salad)
yam ma-muang (green mango salad)

Sauces and Pastes

nahm phrik oong (spicy meat and vegetable sauce)
nahm phrik paw (roasted chilli paste)
phrik gaeng keo wan (green curry paste)
phrik gaeng phed (red curry paste)
poo lon (cooked crabmeat paste or dip)

Soups

khao tom (boiled rice)
tom yum talay (hot and sour seafood soup)

Other Dishes

khao phat supparot (fried rice mixed with
prawn, chicken and pineapple)
tom kem kati pla doog (catfish in turmeric sauce)

NOTES

The shallot is a natural variant of the onion (*Allium cepa* cultivar group Common Onion) and its existence was first noted in 12th-century France. It has since spread throughout the world.

onion plant

onion bulbs

*two onion cultivars, showing side views
and longitudinal sections*

Onion

Scientific or botanical name:
Allium cepa cultivar group
Common Onion

Synonym:
Allium cepa var. *cepa*

**Scientific or botanical
name of family:**
Liliaceae

Common names:
English: onion, common onion,
bulb onion
Thai: *hom-yai* (central Thailand),
hom-huayai (Peninsular Thailand)

Common family name:
lily family

Botanical Description:

The plant is similar to *Allium cepa* (cultivated variety group *Aggregatum*), or shallot, except that the onion plant is larger and has coarser leaves. The mature bulb is also larger and can grow up to 15 cm in diameter, although the shape, size and colour are variable (depending on the cultivated variety).

Like the shallot, this plant is a biennial, meaning the seed will grow into a plant which stores its food in the bulb in the first year, then die down only to grow again, producing flowers, fruits and seeds by using the food reserves in the bulb in the second year. The seeds allow it to reproduce again. Human utilisation, however, exploits this plant as an annual by planting the bulbs to produce more bulbs (asexually), which are then harvested before they produce flowers.

Uses:

The bulb of this plant is used as food, seasoning and spice because of its pungency. The bulbs are used raw, pickled or cooked.

The onion has been used as a diuretic in traditional medicine and recent research has indicated its role in suppressing blood sugar levels and platelet aggregation.

Its flavour and pungency are owed to the presence of S-alk(en)nyl cysteine sulphoxides.

Storage:

Onions are sold with the outer covering dried and can be stored for months in a cool, dry place. The dried outer layers (dried fleshy leaf bases) are removed before use.

In Thai Dishes:

Shallots are preferred to onions in Thai cooking, although it is possible to substitute about six to eight shallots with one medium-sized onion. Nonetheless, there is a distinct difference in taste between the two.

side view and longitudinal section

top, cross-sectional and bottom views

Dishes

gai swam ('heavenly' chicken)
khao phat phrik (chilli fried rice)
laab gai (northeastern chicken salad with mint and lemon grass)
laab neua (northeastern beef salad with mint and lemon grass)
nahm gaeng chud (soup or stock)
nahm phrik pla (spicy fish sauce)
sen mee Krungthep (Bangkok rice noodles, supposedly the inspiration for *mee Siam*, a popular dish in Singapore and Malaysia)
tom yam koong (hot and sour prawn soup)

NOTES

The earliest records of the onion date back to Egypt in 2700 B.C., hence it is safe to assume that domestication of the species must have started even earlier. The crop was introduced by the Romans to Northern and Western Europe in around A.D. 300 and was subsequently introduced to the Americas, Japan and the tropics. It is of some agricultural importance in Thailand, but not in the parts of Southeast Asia that are closer to the equator and have wetter climates.

flowering plant

Spring onion

Scientific or botanical name:
Allium fistulosum

Synonym:
Allium bouddhae

Scientific or botanical name of family:
Liliaceae

Common names:
English: spring onion, scallion, Welsh onion, bunching onion
Thai: *ton-hom* (central Thailand), *hom-chin* (Peninsular Thailand)

Common family name:
lily family

inflorescence

plant as sold in markets

plant base and roots

22

Botanical Description:

The plant is similar in structure to *Allium cepa* (cultivated variety group *Aggregatum*), or shallot, except that the bulbs are indistinct, being narrowly oval or oblong in shape, up to 10 cm long and passing into the green portions of the hollow leaves. The bulbs grow together in a cluster. The inflorescence grows at the tip of the plant and consists of a single stalk that bears numerous flowers or bulbils at the tip. After fertilisation, the flowers become fruits which bear tiny black seeds.

Uses:

The pseudostem region, which is white in colour, rather fleshy and just above the bulb region, consists of concentric sheaths of the leaf bases and are eaten as a vegetable, usually fried with chicken or fish. When the hollow leaves are sliced into short pieces, they become short, hollow cylinders. These are used in salads or to flavour soups and other dishes. This species is less pungent than the *Allium cepa* crops mentioned earlier (shallot and onion).

The mild pungency derives from volatile allyl-sulphides.

Planting this species in gardens can prevent or reduce termite infestation, and the diluted juice pressed from the plants is used to eradicate aphids in China. Chinese traditional medicine uses this plant to improve the functioning of internal organs and metabolism, to improve eyesight, to aid digestion and to improve recovery from colds, headaches, festering sores and wounds.

Storage:

This plant is used fresh so it should be purchased from markets when needed. Rinse the plants to remove dirt and other soil particles and trim off dead or dying leaves before wrapping the plant in dry paper towels. Storing the plant in the vegetable crisper of the refrigerator will keep it fresh for about a week, after which the green upper portions of the leaves will turn yellow and/or dry up.

In Thai Dishes:

The spring onion is a very versatile ingredient in Thai cooking. It can be used as a garnish in almost any dish or used to flavour soups, deep-fried dishes, sauces and stir-fries. The spring onion can also be fashioned into a decorative tassle or flower.

Fried Dishes
taw huu yart sai tort (deep-fried bean curd with crab, pork and spring onions)
thod mun koong (deep-fried prawn balls)

Rice Dishes
joek (rice congee)
khao phat (fried rice)
khao phat phrik (chilli fried rice)

Soups
pet ton hom (duck and spring onion soup)
tom yum talay (hot and sour seafood soup)

Steamed Dishes
bpu tarlae neung (steamed crab)
pla neung khing (steamed fish with ginger sauce)

Other Dishes
nahm pla wan (sweet fish dip for desserts)
pla jian (fish with ginger sauce)

NOTES

Cultivation of the spring onion dates back to at least 200 B.C. in China. It spread to Japan before A.D. 500, after which it spread to Southeast Asia.

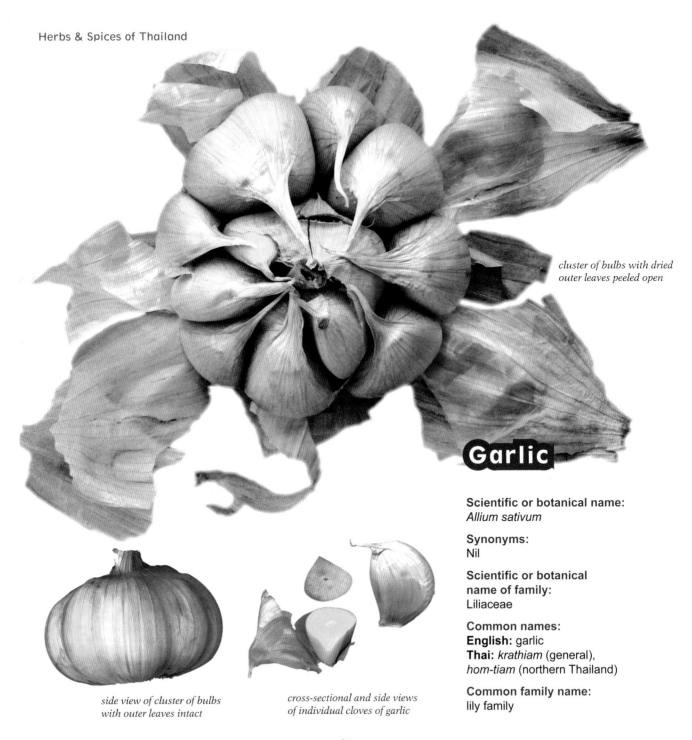

*cluster of bulbs with dried
outer leaves peeled open*

Garlic

*side view of cluster of bulbs
with outer leaves intact*

*cross-sectional and side views
of individual cloves of garlic*

Scientific or botanical name:
Allium sativum

Synonyms:
Nil

**Scientific or botanical
name of family:**
Liliaceae

Common names:
English: garlic
Thai: *krathiam* (general),
hom-tiam (northern Thailand)

Common family name:
lily family

24

Botanical Description:

The plant, which reaches a height of 60 cm, grows from a tight cluster of bulbs, each called a clove. Fibrous roots develop below the bulbs. The whole cluster is flat, round and up to 7 cm in diameter. Each cluster consists of 1 to 15 side bulbs (cloves), which develop from the axillary buds of the leaves of the plant. The leaves overlap concentrically at the base to form a pseudostem, but further towards the tips, they become flat or V-shaped in cross-section. On each plant, there are 4 to 10 leaves growing in two rows. The inflorescence or flowering shoot grows from the bulb and can reach up to 1.5 m. It consists of a single stalk which branches. Each branch bears, in a round mass, bulbils or bulbils and flowers that are covered by a large modified leaf sheath which splits on one side when open. The plant does not produce seeds because the fruits abort.

Uses:

Fresh or dried garlic is used to flavour meat, fish and salads. Of the *Allium* crops, garlic is the second most commonly used after the onion. The bulb and cloves are used, as are the green leaves and immature bulbs.

Garlic is also used medicinally to lower blood sugar and cholesterol levels as well as inhibit thrombus formation. Because of its good health-giving reputation, there are numerous pills, capsules, drinks and powders containing garlic extracts.

The great pungency of the cloves derives from this sequence of events: When the tissues are crushed, an enzyme called allinase is released. This causes the amino acid alliin, also found in the tissues, to become allicin, which is the main cause of the strong smell. To counter 'garlic breath' after consumption of fresh garlic, eat some fresh parsley (*Petroselinum crispum*). When eaten in quantity, the smell of garlic may even be detected in the perspiration of the diner.

Storage:

The dried bulbs are easily purchased from the market and can be kept for months in a cool, dry place.

In Thai Dishes:

Garlic is an almost universal ingredient in Thai cuisine. Only in desserts and cakes does garlic seem to be absent. Although a large quantity of garlic is used in the red and green Thai curry pastes, its flavour is not overwhelming. It also features prominently in the basic *nahm phrik* sauces (hot sauces). The combination of coriander, garlic and peppercorn is classically Thai. It is often used in combination with ginger in fried chicken and pork dishes. Whole pickled garlic bulbs are used as a garnish, while coarsely pounded garlic is used in the signature tangy Thai papaya salad, *som tam*.

Fried and Stir-fried Dishes
panaeng gai (chicken in thick red sauce)
phat kaphrao het (stir-fried mushrooms with chilli and sweet basil)
phat thai (Thai stir-fried rice noodles)
pla meuk thod krathiam phrik (deep-fried squid with garlic and black peppercorns)
pla thod patani (Patani fried fish)

Salads
som tam (spicy papaya salad)
yam pla muk (squid salad)

Sauces and Pastes
gaeng keo wan (Thai green curry)
gaeng phet daeng (Thai red curry)
nahm phrik oong (spicy meat and vegetable sauce)
nahm phrik paw (roasted chilli paste)
nahm phrik plaa (spicy fish sauce)
phat krathiam phrik (fried garlic and chilli)
saos phrik (sweet chilli-garlic sauce)

NOTES

Garlic is such an ancient crop that it was known to be in cultivation in Egypt as far back as 3000 B.C. Like many ancient crops, because it has depended on humankind for propagation, its flowers are no longer functional, and propagation occurs through the planting of the cloves.

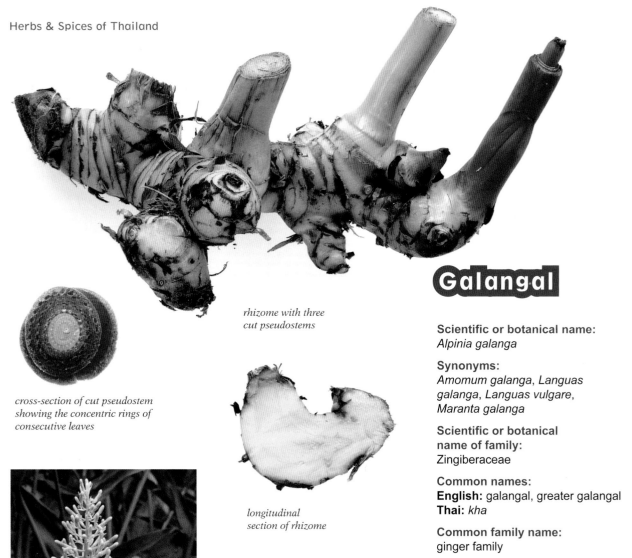

rhizome with three
cut pseudostems

cross-section of cut pseudostem
showing the concentric rings of
consecutive leaves

longitudinal
section of rhizome

inflorescence

Galangal

Scientific or botanical name:
Alpinia galanga

Synonyms:
*Amomum galanga, Languas
galanga, Languas vulgare,
Maranta galanga*

**Scientific or botanical
name of family:**
Zingiberaceae

Common names:
English: galangal, greater galangal
Thai: *kha*

Common family name:
ginger family

Botanical Description:

Galangal is a ginger and the plant has the typical form of one. It grows from a rhizome, which is a stem that grows at or below the soil level. The rhizome is somewhat cylindrical, shortly branched, 2 to 4 cm in diameter, hard, fibrous, shiny light red or pale yellow and fragrant (this being the main part used for flavouring). The leaf scars on the rhizome give it a distinctly striped appearance. Arising from this rhizome are vertical shoots which bear leaves in two rows. These shoots may reach 3.5 m but are usually shorter. Numerous fragrant, yellowish white flowers are borne at the tip of these shoots. After fertilisation, the flowers develop into a round to ellipsoid fruit, 1 to 1.5 cm in diameter, turning orange red to dark red when ripe.

Uses:

The rhizome of galangal is the main part of the plant that is used as a spice. Its scent is difficult to describe but approximately resembles a mixture of pepper and common ginger, although much more pleasant and invigorating. Besides this, the flowers and young shoots may also be used as a spice or vegetable. The fruits may be substituted for the fruits of the true cardamom since they are similar in taste.

The rhizome has also been used for various traditional medical treatments, such as cancers of the mouth and stomach, colic, dysentery, indigestion, enlarged spleen, respiratory diseases, skin diseases, systemic infections, cholera, as an expectorant, as a tonic after childbirth, as a stimulant or aphrodisiac and even in veterinary medicine.

The flavouring scent comes from the essential oil extracted from the rhizome. This oil has been used to flavour ice-cream, liqueurs, pastry and other foods. One can extract the oil quite easily by grinding the rhizome and mixing the pulp with hot water. This aqueous mixture can act as an insect repellent or insecticide for garden plants.

Essential oil content is about 0.1% fresh weight, and 0.2 to 1.5% dry weight of the rhizome. The essential oil is reported to be mainly cineole. Other compounds isolated from the rhizome have been shown to be antibacterial, antifungal, antiprotozoal and antitumour in activity.

Storage:

Galangal is used fresh so the rhizomes should be purchased from markets for use whenever needed. After purchase, they may be stored in the refrigerator's vegetable crisper, wrapped in paper to absorb excess moisture. This way, the rhizomes should last about a week.

Rhizomes also tend to dry out quickly so wrapping them prevents excessive desiccation. Because of the need to use fresh rhizomes, this spice is often cultivated in kitchen gardens. Best quality is achieved by harvesting three months after planting pieces of the rhizome purchased from the market.

In Thai Dishes:

Galangal is most prominent in the *tom kha* soups (coconut milk and galangal-based soups). In a *tom kha* soup, the galangal gives a peppery taste and sour finish that interplays very well with the creamy coconut milk. Galangal is an essential spice in the three famous *gaengs*, or Thai curry pastes (*gaeng panaeng*, or Thai Penang curry; *gaeng keo wan*, or Thai green curry; and *gaeng phet daeng*, or Thai red curry). Galangal water can be made by mixing pounded galangal with water and adding some salt. This can be used in a dressing for salads to offset any strong-tasting meats used (such as liver).

Soups
tom kha gai (spicy chicken, galangal
and coconut milk soup)
tom kha phak (vegetable, galangal
and coconut milk soup)
(Any other ingredients including fish, seafood or
mushroom can feature in a *tom kha* soup.)

Other Dishes
koong korat (prawn in spicy sauce)
phrik gaeng — curry pastes, including *gaeng panaeng*
(Thai Penang curry), *gaeng keo wan* (Thai green curry)
and *gaeng phet daeng* (Thai red curry)
thod mun pla (deep-fried fish cakes)
tom kem kati pla doog (catfish in turmeric sauce)

NOTES

Like many species which are cultivated, the exact origins of galangal are not known, although the oldest records mentioning its use come from Java and southern China. The plant is now grown as a crop in Bangladesh, China, India, Southeast Asia and Surinam.

Chinese keys

Scientific or botanical name:
Boesenbergia rotunda

Synonyms:
Boesenbergia pandurata, *Cucurma rotunda*, *Gastrochilus pandurata*, *Kaempferia pandurata*

Scientific or botanical name of family:
Zingiberaceae

Common names:
English: Chinese keys, Chinese key, finger root, resurrection lily, tropical crocus
Thai: *krachai, khao chae* (general), *ka-en* (northern Thailand), *wan-phraathit* (Bangkok)

Common family name:
ginger family

rhizome with cut pseudostems and long fleshy roots growing downwards

28

Botanical Description:

The plant is a herbaceous perennial that grows from a rhizome from which leafy shoots arise and roots develop below. The leafy shoots grow to a height of 30 to 80 cm and bear three to seven leaves in the upper portion and three bladeless sheaths below. The leaves are alternately arranged in two rows, each leaf consisting of a sheath at the bottom, an erect stalk up to 30 cm high and an elliptical-oblong to broadly lance-shaped leaf blade which can grow up to 50 cm long and 17 cm wide. The concentric sheaths of consecutive leaves — the sheaths are vertical and wrap around each other like the parts of the aerial of a car radio — form a pseudostem, which is the axis of the leafy shoot. The rhizome at the bottom of the leafy shoot consists of a number of merged, round joints which are yellowish brown on the outside and bright yellow on the inside. The roots, which develop from the rhizome, are fleshy and club-like. The common name 'Chinese keys' refers to the roots which resemble the keys the ancient Chinese used. The inflorescence, or flowering shoot, develops at the tip of the leafy shoot, consisting of an axis 10 to 15 cm long, bearing about 10 stalked flowers which hardly exceed the leaf sheaths of the uppermost leaves. Each flower consists of sepals and petals which join together to form a 6 cm-long tube. At the tip of this tube are three oblong, 1.7 cm-long pink lobes and a pink and white or pure pink lip that is spotted red-violet within. The flower's sterile stamens resemble pink petals, with one stamen having a white filament and yellowish white anther. The fruit is unknown in this species.

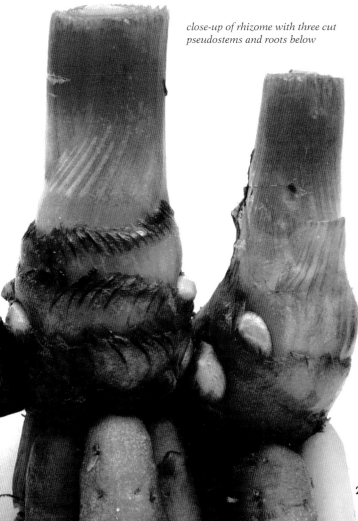

close-up of rhizome with three cut pseudostems and roots below

Uses:

The highly aromatic rhizome and tuberous roots are used as a spicy flavouring for food and pickles, eaten raw with rice (in Malaysia) or its young shoots eaten raw with rice (in Java, Indonesia). Its leaves are used together with those of teak (*Tectona grandis*) to wrap fungus-fermented soya beans (*tempeh*) in East Java.

The essential oil from the rhizomes and roots that are largely responsible for the strong aroma in this plant consists of the following components: 1,8-cineole (18 to 41%), camphor (13%), d-borneol (9.2%), d-pinene (4.1%), zingiberene (2.7%) and other minor components.

close-up of root longitudinal sections

In traditional medicine, the rhizomes and roots are used in postpartum tonics, as a stomachic and carminative, as well as a remedy for coughs, indigestion, sprue and colic. They are also used in the treatment for ringworm, rheumatic and postpartum muscular pains, swollen abdomen and urination difficulty in children.

Storage:

The rhizome and roots can be rinsed under the tap and then blotted dry with paper towels. The plant parts should keep for about a week when wrapped in dry paper and placed in the refrigerator's vegetable crisper. To store for longer periods, divide the rhizome and roots into portions which you will use in your cooking and freeze them. They should keep for months since the aroma (which comes from the volatile oils) is retained when frozen.

In Thai Dishes:

Chinese keys impart a peppery and camphor-like flavour to dishes, initially sharp but becoming smooth later. It is useful in Thai curry pastes (*gaeng*) and is an especially important ingredient in the 'jungle' curry (*gaeng bpa-moo*), as well as in relishes (*lon*). Almost all parts of the plant are used in the original recipe of the hot and tangy salad, *yam krachai*.

Curry and other Pastes
gaeng keo wan (Thai green curry)
gaeng bpa moo ('jungle' curry)
lon gapi (prawn paste simmered in coconut cream)
phrik gaeng (Thai curry pastes)

Other Dishes
gaeng liang pla (fish and vegetable curry)
thod mun pla (deep-fried fish cakes)
yam krachai gap koong warn (wild ginger and sweet prawn salad)

NOTES

Chinese keys originate from Java and Sumatra, Indonesia, but are cultivated in India, Sri Lanka, Southeast Asia (in particular, Indonesia, Malaysia and Thailand) and southern China.

longitudinal sections,
root cut into three portions and
cross-sections of root at the cut positions

*side view and
cross-section of
fruit and seeds*

packaged dried chillies

Scientific or botanical name:
Capsicum annuum var. *annuum*
Capsicum frutescens

Synonyms:
For *Capsicum annuum*: Nil
For *Capsicum frutescens*: Nil

**Scientific or botanical
name of family**:
Solanaceae

Common names:
For *Capsicum annuum* var. *annuum*
English: chilli, capsicum, cayenne
pepper, pepper
Thai: *phrik, phrik chii faa*

For *Capsicum frutescens*
English: bird pepper, bird's eye
chilli, chilli, capsicum pepper
Thai: *phrik, phrik khii nuu*

Common family name:
potato family

Chilli & Bird pepper

Botanical Description:

Capsicum annuum var. *annuum*: The 0.5 to 1.5 m-tall plant is an annual and consists of a single stem from which many branches grow upwards and a branching taproot that grows into the ground. The branches bear alternate leaves. Each leaf has a stalk up to 10 cm long and an egg-shaped leaf blade that can grow up to 16 cm long by 8 cm wide. At each leaf axil, one flower usually develops (rarely two or more). Each flower has a drooping stalk and a green, cup-shaped calyx with fine 'teeth' at its rim, extending from the veins. The petals are white or milky white (rarely purple) and are joined into a bell-shaped structure with five to seven 'teeth' at the rim. On each flower, there are five to seven stamens with pale blue to violet anthers and a pistil which consists of a knob-like stigma. A narrow, tubular style connects the stigma to the ovary. The fruit usually hangs downwards and is of rather variable pungency, colour, size and shape, although it is more commonly an elongated,

32

chilli powder

fried bird pepper with garlic mixture

The fruit is usually held vertically upwards (for better presentation to fruit-eating birds which are the main dispersers in nature), up to 5 cm long by 1 cm wide (but usually smaller), spindle-shaped or narrowly conical. When unripe, the fruits are green to cream or yellow; when ripe, they are orange then finally red. The seeds are round, flat and straw-coloured, and many are yielded on each fruit.

The differences between *Capsicum annuum* var. *annuum* and *Capsicum frutescens* are outlined in the table below.

Capsicum annuum var. *annuum*	Capsicum frutescens
At each node, one flower (occasionally two or more)	At each node, two flowers (occasionally one or more than two)
The flower stalk points downwards at flowering.	The flower stalk is erect at flowering but the tip bends downwards.
The fruit hangs downwards.	The fruit is usually held vertically upwards.
The corolla is white to milky white (occasionally purple).	The corolla is greenish white.
The corolla lobes are usually straight.	The corolla lobes are often slightly rolled backwards.
The calyx of the mature fruit is sometimes irregularly wrinkled.	The calyx of the mature fruit is usually irregularly wrinkled.
The calyx veins often extend into short 'teeth'.	The calyx veins do not extend into short 'teeth'.
The fruit flesh is firm (but soft in some cultivated varieties).	The fruit flesh is always soft.

spindle shape or somewhat conical. It may grow up to 20 cm long or more (but is usually shorter). When unripe, the fruits are usually shiny green; on ripening, they turn from purplish to red or orange. The seeds are round, flat, 3 to 4 mm in diameter and straw-coloured, and many are yielded in each fruit.

Capsicum frutescens: Up to 1 m tall, this species is a perennial and consists of a single stem that bears many branches and grows from a taproot. The plant lives for two to three years. The branches bear alternate leaves; each leaf has a stalk and an egg-shaped leaf blade up to 10 cm long by 5 cm wide. At each leaf axil, usually two flowers (sometimes more or only one) form. The flower is similar to that of the *Capsicum annuum* var. *annuum*, except that the erect stalk bends at its tips.

range of different sizes of dried chillies

Uses:

For both species, the ripe or unripe fruit is used fresh, pickled or dried (only when ripe) and processed. Raw fruit slices in soy or fish sauce are eaten with various cooked dishes.

The hot-spiciness, or pungency, derives from the capsaicinoids (alkaloids) in the cross-walls and placental tissues of the fruit. If one cores out the centre of fruit which consists of the placenta (the tissues to which the seeds are attached), the cross-walls (partitions) and the seeds, then discards them, the remainder outer fruit wall will hardly be spicy-hot. The larger the chilli, the easier it is to core out the placenta and cross-walls without contaminating the remainder of the chilli with the capsaicinoids.

Storage:

Fresh chilli fruits, if left outside, tend to dry up. Rinse the fruits with tap water, blot completely dry with paper towels and then wrap in dry paper towels. Place the wrapped chilli fruits in a plastic food storage container before putting them in the vegetable crisper of a refrigerator. When kept in large quantities together, the condensation from the fruits causes fungal growth, so keeping them dry with paper or towelling to absorb excess moisture is important. Kept this way, they can last up to five weeks.

In Thai Dishes:

It is surprising that the chilli has had a relatively short history in Thailand. It was only introduced by the Portuguese in the early 1600s and in a few short decades spread to all parts of the country.

Thai cuisine is almost synonymous with the pungency of chillies. There are a few varieties that are commonly used in Thai cuisine and the two most popular ones are the *phrik chii faa* and the *phrik khii nuu*. The pungency of chillies can be measured in Scoville units, after Wilbur Scoville who came up with the test in 1912. The higher the unit, the greater the hot-spicy pungency. The *phrik chii faa* scores 35,000 to 45,000 units while the *phrik khii nuu* scores 60,000 to 80,000 units.

Essentially, the *phrik chii faa* (literally meaning 'sky pointing chilli') are finger-length chillies and the *phrik khii nuu* are the smaller (hence the name which literally means 'mouse dropping chilli') yet viciously pungent chillies.

The *phrik chii faa* is long and slender (6 to 10 cm long) and has red, green and yellow cultivated varieties. The seeds of this variety are also hard to chew. Highly prized by the Thais, the red *phrik chii faa* is the main chilli ingredient in most curry pastes (for this, the dried chillies are used).

The *phrik khii nuu* (bird pepper) is tiny, 1 to 2 cm long, torpedo-shaped and twice as hot as the *phrik chii faa*. It tends to be eaten fresh and whole like in the famous *miang kham* (spicy leaf-wrapped tidbits). They also typify hot Thai dishes such as the *nahm phrik* (relishes), the Thai *yam* and *laab* salads and, of course, the famous *tom yam* soups (hot and sour soups). The curries (*gaeng phet daeng*, or red curry paste; *gaeng som*, or tamarind-flavoured soup) utilise mainly the *phrik chii faa*, although the green curries and southern or northeastern curries that utilise the *phrik khii nuu* tend to be hotter. The *tom yam* soups are typically very pungent and these usually have bruised *phrik khii nuu*.

Dishes, Pastes and Sauces

For *phrik chii faa*:

gway tio phat khi mao talay (spicy fried
rice noodles with seafood)

nahm phrik (basic hot sauce; dried *phrik
chii faa* is used here as well as fresh *phrik
khii nuu* for that extra heat)

neua phat phrik (stir-fried beef with chillies)

phat kaphrao het (stir-fried mushrooms
with chilli and sweet basil)

phrik gaeng (Thai curry pastes)

phrik siyu wan (chopped chillies
in sweet Chinese soy sauce)

tom kha gai (spicy chicken, galangal
and coconut milk soup)

For *phrik khii nuu*:

gaeng chud muea bpu saku (pork,
crabmeat and tapioca soup)

gaeng keo wan (green curry)

gaeng tom yam gai (hot and sour
chicken soup with lemon grass)

nahm phrik (hot sauce)

nahm phrik oong (spicy meat and vegetable sauce)

nahm phrik paw (roasted chilli paste)

nahm phrik pla (spicy fish sauce)

nahm pla phrik khii nuu (fish sauce
with bird peppers)

tom yam koong (hot and sour prawn soup)

tom yam neua (hot and sour beef soup)

tom yam pla muk (hot and sour stuffed squid soup)

NOTES

The cultivated species of *Capsicum* include *Capsicum annuum*, *Capsicum baccatum*, *Capsicum chinense*, *Capsicum frutescens* and *Capsicum pubescens*. There are about 16 species which are strictly wild and not used by people.

Among all, *Capsicum annuum* is the most widely cultivated and most economically important species. This species, in turn, consists of two botanical varieties: *Capsicum annuum* var. *annuum*, which includes all the cultivated members of the species, and *Capsicum annuum* var. *glabrisculum*, which includes all the wild members of the species. There are numerous cultivated varieties of *Capsicum annuum* var. *annuum*. However, as there has been little agreement on how to classify these, there is some confusion owing to the great variation in the fruit size, colour and shape. Hence, in this book, there is no attempt to name the different kinds of chillies found in Thai markets.

The chilli fruit cannot ripen when detached from the plant so do not expect unripe fruit (green or cream) to ripen to orange or red by storing it for prolonged periods or even inducing ripening through ethylene gas (plant-ripening hormone) by exposing the chilli fruit to fruits that produce a lot of ethylene (such as apples or bananas). Bird pepper fruits are apparently immune to ethylene so the fruits will ultimately rot instead.

The capsaicinoids which cause the pungency or spicy-hotness are not water but fat (hence oil-soluble) so it is less effective to drink water to relieve oneself of the 'burning' sensation on eating chillies of high pungency. The trick is to swirl milk or ice-cream in one's mouth since the butterfat in the milk or ice-cream will dissolve the capsaicinoids out from the lining of the mouth and tongue.

People enjoy eating capsaicinoids because they cause endorphins to be released, something that is pleasantly stimulating — hence the popularity of bird peppers or chillies in diets of people wherever these crops have been introduced.

*bird peppers (left four) and chilli
cultivated varieties (right five)*

Chinese cassia bark strips

Cinnamon

Scientific or botanical name:
Cinnamomum burmanni
Cinnamomum cassia
Cinnamomum loureirii

Synonyms:
For *Cinnamomum burmanni*:
Cinnamomum mindnaense,
Laurus burmanni

For *Cinnamomum cassia*:
Cinnamomum aromaticum,
Laurus cassia

For *Cinnamomum loureirii*:
Cinnamomum obtusifolium

Scientific or botanical name of family: Lauraceae

Common names:
For *Cinnamomum burmanni*:
English: cassia or cinnamon (general name for all cassias), Indonesian cassia, Batavia cassia, Batavia cinnamon, Java cassia, Padang cassia, Padang cinnamon
Thai: *suramarit* (Nakhon Ratchasima in northeast Thailand)

For *Cinnamomum cassia*:
English: cassia or cinnamon (general name for all cassias), Chinese cassia, Chinese cinnamon, cassia lignea
Thai: *kaeng* (Chiang Mai)

For *Cinnamomum loureirii*:
English: cassia or cinnamon (general name for all cassias), Vietnamese cassia, Saigon cassia, Saigon cinnamon
Thai: *obchoey* (Bangkok)

Common family name:
laurel family

*Indonesian cassia
bark quills*

Botanical Description:
All three species are evergreen, aromatic shrubs or trees with smooth bark. The branches bear stalked, alternate to opposite leaves with leaf blades that have one central mid-rib and two lateral veins towards the margins. When crushed, the leaves are aromatic because of the glands in the tissues. The many-flowered inflorescences grow from the axils of the leaves or branch tips. Each flower consists of six tepals which join together at the base, nine stamens, three staminodes (sterile stamens) and a pistil. The pistil consists of an ovary that is connected to a slender style which is, in turn, topped by a discoid or somewhat three-lobed stigma. The fruit is a one-seeded, globose to cylindrical berry.

The differences between the three species are shown in the table below.

Characteristics	*Cinnamomum burmanni* (Indonesian cassia)	*Cinnamomum cassia* (Chinese cassia)	*Cinnamomum loureirri* (Vietnamese cassia)
Plant type	Shrub or small tree (up to 15 m tall)	Tree (up to 18 m tall)	Tree (8 to 10 m tall)
Arrangement of leaves	Somewhat oppositely arranged	Alternately to almost oppositely arranged	Oppositely or alternately arranged
Leaf	Oblong-elliptical to lance-shaped, 4 to 14 cm long by 1.5 to 6 cm wide, glossy green above and with a white waxy bloom on the underside	Oblong-elliptical, 8 to 20 cm long by 4 to 7.5 cm wide, dark shiny green above and lighter green on the underside	Elliptical to oblong-shaped, 7.5 to 12.5 cm long by 3 to 5 cm wide, green above and lighter green on the underside
Fruit	Ovoid, about 1 cm long	Ovoid to ellipsoid, 1 to 1.5 cm long	Similar but smaller than that of *Cinnamomum cassia*
Distribution and cultivation	Naturally distributed in Malesia and commercially cultivated in Java and Sumatra in Indonesia and in the Philippines	Naturally distributed in southern China, Myanmar, Laos and Vietnam and commercially cultivated in China and Vietnam	Naturally distributed in the mountains of Annam (Vietnam) and commercially cultivated in Vietnam

trunk of Indonesian cassia

leafy branches of Indonesian cassia

*Inflorescences and young reddish leaves of wild cinnamon (*Cinnamomum iners)*, a related species*

Uses:

The dried inner bark of all three species is used for flavouring home-cooked or industrially prepared food. Distilled bark oil and oleoresin (from solvent extraction) are also used, the former in soaps and perfumes and the latter in flavouring processed foods.

Powdered cassia bark, as noted in the *British Herbal Pharmacopoeia*, is used as a cure for colic with nausea and flatulent dyspepsia, as well as in folk medicine cures for coughs, chest complaints, diarrhoea, gripe and malaria. Cassia oil is also noted for its antibacterial, carminative and fungistatic uses and for improving appetite and dyspeptic disturbances.

The light- to medium-weight hardwood timber from the *Cinnamomum* species (camphor wood) is used in making decorative work and furniture and can be used for plywood manufacture or moth-proof chests because of its fragrance. In Malaysia, *Cinnamomum* timber is traded under the Malay timber name *medang*, together with the timbers of other members of its family. *Cinnamomum* trees are also cultivated as wayside trees along roads or as shade trees (e.g., *Cinnamomum burmanni* in Indonesia, *Cinnamomum iners* in Singapore).

For *Cinnamomum burmanni*, only the bark is economically important, with Padang (western Sumatra, Indonesia) being an important area of production. The bark contains 1 to 4% essential oil. The main constituent of the essential oil is cinnamaldehyde, which gives it its aroma.

For *Cinnamomum cassia*, only the bark and leaf oil are economically important. The Chinese provinces of Kwangsi and Kwangtung are the main areas of production and export. Distillation of the leaves and twigs of *Cinnamomum cassia* produces cassia leaf oil for perfumes and flavouring, especially in cola drinks. Dried, immature buds of this species (cassia buds, *bunga lawang*, etc.), with a cinnamon scent and sweet pungent flavour, are used as flavouring in dishes such as sweet pickles. The bark contains 1 to 4% essential oil. The bark and leaf oil have similar constituents, being 70 to 95% cinnamaldehyde with only traces of eugenol.

For *Cinnamomum loureirii*, only the bark is economically important, with Vietnam being the main producer and exporter. The bark contains 1 to 7% essential oil. Like *Cinnamomum cassia*, the bark oil consists mainly of cinnamaldehyde with traces of eugenol.

Storage:
The dried bark of the three cassia species comes in rolled quills which can be stored for several months in a cool, dry place. Grind the bark for use only when needed so that the aroma is not lost.

In Thai Dishes:
Cassia is used mostly in curries, especially those of Arab origins, such as the *gaeng mussaman* which literally means 'Muslim curry'.

Curries
gaeng hang lae (northern pork curry)
gaeng mussaman gai (Muslim curry with chicken)
gaeng mussaman neua (Muslim curry with beef)
gaeng phet taet (hot and sour prawn
and cucumber curry)

Other Dishes
khao buri ('city' rice)
khao mok gai (Muslim dish of chicken braised
in rice with turmeric and spices)
khao soy (curry noodles from the Tai people,
an ethnic group living in southern China,
parts of Indochina and South Asia)
phrik kaeng gai kung (spicy braised chicken)
peanut sauce for *satay* (Thai recipe)

NOTES
True cinnamon (*Cinnamomum verum* or *Cinnamomum zeylanicum*, as it is known in older literature) is native to southwest India, western Sri Lanka (Ceylon) and the Tenasserim Hills of Myanmar (Burma). This species is cultivated in Madagascar, the Seychelles, southern India and Sri Lanka, which is the main producer. The constituents of the essential oil for the true cinnamon species is similar to those of the cassia, hence the barks of cassia and cinnamon are interchangeable for many applications. In Southeast Asia, cassia bark is used mainly for cooking.

*Indonesian cassia bark quills
and their cross-sections*

Kaffir lime

Scientific or botanical name:
Citrus hystrix

Synonyms: Nil

Scientific or botanical name of family:
Rutaceae

Common names:
English: kaffir lime
Thai: *magrut* (general)

Common family name:
orange family

cross-section of kaffir lime fruit

bottom, top and side views

top and underside of the leaf

Botanical Description:

A very thorny shrub, this plant measures from 3.0 to 4.6 m or more in height but is often grown short for easy harvesting of its leaves. The alternate leaves are very characteristic, with leaf stalks that are broadly winged. The stalk can be narrower to almost as wide as the actual leaf such that the stalk looks like another leaf blade. Leaf blades are about 2.5 to 10 cm long and about as broad. The wing and blade margins are notched (meaning the sinuses between lobes are very narrow and shallow, like a notch). Leaves are dotted with minute oil glands, smelling distinctively of citronella when crushed. The flowers have four to six white petals clustered in the leaf axils. The flowers have numerous stamens, which is characteristic of the family. The green fruit is round, up to 3.5 to 7.5 cm across, extremely wrinkly or bumpy and is bitter and slightly fragrant.

Uses:

One of the chief traditional uses of the fruit among the Malays is in washing the hair and body, although this practice is not as widespread today. The peel and fruit juice were used in *ubat jamu*, a tonic that was believed to drive away evil spirits. In traditional Malay medicine, the fruit is used to treat stomach pains, and the rind used for headaches and against worms in children. The juice is also used to flavour sauces but only in small amounts as it has a very acidic taste.

A volatile oil can be distilled from the leaves. The leaves are very aromatic and readily impart a flavour to foods. They feature very widely in Thai cuisine.

Its timber can be used in making tool handles.

Storage:

Fresh kaffir lime leaves are prone to drying out, whether placed in the open or in a refrigerator. When storing in the latter, rinse leaves with tap water, dab dry with paper towels, then wrap in dry paper or paper towels and place all the leaves in a plastic food container or re-sealable plastic bag. Keep the container or bag in the vegetable crisper of the refrigerator, where it will keep for about a week. Alternatively, for longer-term storage, rinse with tap water, dab dry and then store twigs with leaves or leaves alone in a plastic container in the freezer section where they will keep for months. Before cooking, thaw out the amount needed. Freezing keeps the aromatic essential oil, which defines this spice, from evaporating.

In Thai Dishes:

The leaf, or sometimes the grated zest of the fruit wall, is used to give that refreshing lemony flavour to many Thai dishes, especially curry pastes, soups and stocks. It is said to give added fragrance to a curry. The finely shredded leaves of the kaffir lime are used as an ingredient in the distinctive Thai *yam* salads and the juice of the knobby-skinned fruit is sometimes used in salad dressings.

upper portion of a leafy branch

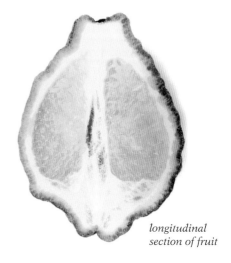

longitudinal section of fruit

Curries
gaeng keo wan (Thai green curry)
gaeng panaeng (Thai Penang curry)
gaeng phet korat (Korat beef curry)

Salads
yam nang muu (pork rind with lemon grass salad)
yam neua (beef salad)

Soups
All *tom yam* soups such as
nahm gaeng chud (soup or stock)
tom kha phak (vegetable, galangal
and coconut milk soup)
tom yam koong (hot and sour prawn soup)
tom yam neua (hot and sour beef soup)
tom yam pla muk (hot and sour stuffed squid soup)

Other Dishes
haw moak (steamed curried fish cake)
saeng wa koong pao (blanched prawn seasoned with
chilli, onion and lemon grass)
thod mun pla (deep-fried fish cakes)

NOTES

Of the *Citrus* species, the kaffir lime is so distinct that some taxonomists have considered placing it in a separate genus, but current consensus is that it should stay in *Citrus*.

leafy branch showing thorns in the axils

kaffir lime bush

longitudinal section and side view of Buddha's hand citron fruit

upper side of leaf

flowers and leaves at branch tip

citron fruit on branch tip

Citron

Scientific or botanical name:
Citrus medica

Synonyms:
Citrus aurantium var. *medica*,
Citrus crassa

**Scientific or botanical
name of family:**
Rutaceae

Common names:
English: citron
Thai: *manao-khwai* (Yala-Pattani
provinces), *soma-ngua* (central
Thailand), *mwo-yao* (Chiang Mai)

Common family name:
orange family

Botanical Description:

The plant is a straggly shrub or small tree, growing up to 3 m tall. When grown from seed, it starts to fruit at three years, peaks at 15 and dies at 25. The bark is light grey in colour and the wood is relatively soft. Twigs are angular in cross-section and purplish when young but become circular when older. Thorns are found in the leaf axils (angles where the leaves are connected to the twigs or branches). The stalked leaves have elliptical to egg-shaped to lance-shaped leaf blades, which range from 5 to 20 cm long by 3 to 9 cm wide. The blade margins are shallowly toothed. The few-flowered inflorescences develop at leaf axils. The flowers are 3 to 4 cm in diameter, and each consists of five sepals, five pink petals, 30 to 60 stamens and a pistil, which in turn consists of an ovary with a thick style and blunt stigma at its tip. The fruit is an oval- to oblong-shaped berry, 10 to 20 cm long and essentially similar in structure to an orange or pomelo (except for the thicker peel). The exterior of the peel is rough and covered with tiny bumps, green when unripe and yellow when ripe after about three months, and the peel is fragrant and very thick. The small segments are filled with juice vesicles which are pale green. The juice is slightly sour to sweet. There are numerous oval seeds which are about 1 cm long by 0.5 cm across.

Uses:

The fruit, and in particular the candied peel, is used in cakes and confectioneries. To make candied citron, green fruits are halved by slicing, and allowed to ferment for a month or more in barrels of brine, after which they are rinsed and placed in more salt solution. After partial salt removal and boiling to soften the peel, they are placed in a concentrated sugar solution to produce the candied peels. The strong aroma comes from the essential oils in the peel, especially at the outermost layer where the numerous glands in the bumps are found.

There are two groups of cultivated varieties, i.e., the acid cultivars (with light pink flower buds and shoots, sour pulp and a dark inner seed coat) and the non-acid ones (sweet pulp and a colourless inner seed coat, without the light pink flower buds and shoots).

In China, Japan, Indo-China and India, a special variety of this species, *Citrus medica* var. *sarcodactylis*, is cultivated for the closed hand-like fruits called the 'fingered citron' or 'Buddha's hand citron' (*som-mu* in Thai). Its fragrance and beauty are highly regarded and the fruit is used to provide scent to clothing and rooms. In the Far East, this variety, grown as a dwarf plant, is highly valued as an ornamental plant.

Since Roman times, the fruits have been used to flavour food, as a moth repellent and also in perfumes. The fresh flowers, fruits, leaves, seeds and shoots have been used in traditional medical treatments for arthritis, asthma, backache, headache, stomachache, intestinal parasites, respiratory problems and psychological disorders (including insanity and possession by evil spirits).

Storage:

The fruit is best used fresh and can be stored at room temperature in a fruit basket for about a week.

In Thai Dishes:

The juice and the zest are used. The sweet-sour juice may be used in combination with other citrus juices or with tamarind juice in salad dressings.

Dishes and Relish
nahm phrik koong haeng (prawn paste relish)
nahm phrik lon pak ruu (minced prawns simmered in coconut cream and chilli)
saeng wa koong pao (blanched prawn seasoned with chilli, onion and lemon grass)
yam piu som sa gap pla grop (salad of crispy fish and citron zest)

NOTES

This species is rather delicate and hence more suited to cultivation in home gardens than in commercial orchards.

Coriander

Scientific or botanical name:
Coriandrum sativum

Synonyms:
Coriandrum diversifolium,
Coriandrum globosum, Coriandrum
majus, Coriandrum testiculatum

**Scientific or botanical
name of family:**
Apiaceae or Umbelliferae

Common names:
English: coriander (fruits/seeds,
leaves, roots), cilantro (leaves),
Chinese parsley (leaves)
Thai: *phakom* (northern Thailand),
phakom-noi (northeastern Thailand),
phakchi (central Thailand)

Common family name:
celery family

coriander plant

46

*lower portions of plants
showing tops of roots*

Botanical Description:

This annual plant consists of a short, erect stem, which produces many branches. At which base is a well-developed and branching taproot growing downwards. Plants can grow up to 1.3 m tall. The stalked leaves are arranged alternately, with the lower ones simple (the leaf blade in one piece), but the upper ones once-pinnate or twice-pinnate, with leaflets (pinnae) or second order leaflets (pinnules), respectively. The inflorescence is a compound structure, bearing numerous flowers in spherical bunches. The flowers are usually bisexual, with the central ones being male. After fertilisation, the flowers develop into an oval to round fruit up to 5 mm in diameter. Each fruit contains two seeds.

Uses:

Dried coriander fruits are used as a spice. The fresh whole plants and leaves are used as a culinary herb or vegetable. The fresh taproot is even more aromatic than the stems or leaves and is used in China, Thailand and other Southeast Asian countries in flavouring. The dried green plants and the dried fruits are traded in commerce.

The essential oil content of fruits varies from trace amounts to 2% of the air-dried weight and consists of mainly linalool (60%), numerous monoterpenoids and minor components such as camphor, geraniol, geranyl acetate, pinene and terpinene. The aroma of coriander comes from about 41 volatile components detected in the essential oil of the leaf, with aldehydes making up more than 80% of these.

Coriander has been used in folk medicine since ancient times. The application of the green plants as a cure for measles is an East Asian practice. The fruits have been noted to have antibilous, anticatarrhal, antispasmodic, aphrodisiac, carminative, diuretic, emmenagogue, galactogogue, refrigerant, stomachic and tonic effects. The essential oil extracted from the fruits is used to flavour foods, in medicine and perfumes, while the remaining (extracted) fruit is used to feed cattle.

close-up of dried fruits

Storage:

Dried coriander fruit is best kept in an airtight container in a cool, dry place. The fresh plants should be kept intact in the refrigerator. First, rinse plants with tap water to remove soil particles. Then dab dry with paper towels and wrap with dry paper or paper towels in a re-sealable plastic bag or food container to store in the refrigerator's vegetable crisper. This should last about a week.

In Thai Dishes:

The leaf and the roots of the coriander are essential to Thai cuisine. The seeds are also used, but only to a certain extent. The fresh leaves are very often used as garnishes in soups, salads, fried and stir-fried dishes and especially in conjunction with seafood. Handfuls of the leaves are used in combination with mint leaves in salads for a light refreshing taste. The leaves are used in the popular Thai street salad snack, *miang kham* (spicy leaf-wrapped tidbits). The root is usually pounded with garlic and pepper as a classic base for many Thai dishes. The root is also scraped and used as an important ingredient in salad dressings. Both the root and seeds are essential in curry pastes.

Salads
laab gai (northeastern chicken salad with
mint, onion and lemon grass)
laab neau (northeastern beef salad with
mint, onion and lemon grass)
miang kham (spicy leaf-wrapped tidbits)
yam hoi nang rom (oyster salad)

Soups
gaeng chud no mai (bamboo shoot and pork soup,
using the whole plant, including the root)
gaeng tom sum (sour pork and
vegetable soup, using the root)
nahm gaeng chud (soup or stock, using the root)
tom kha gai (spicy chicken, galangal
and coconut milk soup)
tom kha phak (vegetable, galangal
and coconut milk soup)
tom yam koong (hot and sour prawn soup)
tom yum talay (hot and sour seafood soup)

Other Dishes
gaeng keo wahn loogchin pla/koong
(Thai green curry with fish/prawn dumplings,
using the coriander seeds)
gway tio neua (beef and noodle soup)
phrik gaeng (Thai curry pastes, using seeds and root)
pla jian (fish with ginger sauce,
using the leaf as garnish)
peanut sauce for *satay* (Thai recipe,
using the fruits)

NOTES

Coriander is a variable species with a number of groups or subspecies. The Thai idiom *phak chii rohy naa* (literally "coriander leaf sprinkled on top") means to perform a deed only for the sake of appearance.

leaflets of coriander leaf

dried cumin fruits

ground cumin fruits

dried caraway fruits (commonly mistaken for cumin)

ground caraway fruits

close-up of split cumin fruits

Cumin

Scientific or botanical name:
Cuminum cyminum

Synonyms:
Cuminum odorum,
Ligusticum cuminum

Scientific or botanical name of family:
Apiaceae or Umbelliferae

Common Names:
English: cumin, Roman caraway
Thai: *thian kao*, *yira* (general)

Common family name:
celery family

Botanical Description:

The plant is an annual herb that is erect to slightly leaning, and ranges from 20 to 80 cm in height. The somewhat cylindrical stem is 3 mm in diameter, branching at all levels along its length, and has a thin taproot growing into the soil. A waxy bloom covers all green parts of the plant. The alternate, blue-green, stalked leaves have blades which are each divided into three narrow and elongated leaflets. These are further forked two to three times into lobes up to 7 cm long. The inflorescence consists of clusters of flowers whose stalks arise from the top of a main stalk.

Uses:

Throughout the world, the fruits are used, in small quantities, for flavouring breads, cheeses, chutneys, meat dishes, pickles, rice, salad dressings, sauerkraut, sausages, soups and stews. Egyptian, Indian and Turkish curry and chilli powder mixtures have the ground fruits as an ingredient. The essential oil extracted from the fruit is found in various food products, liqueurs and perfumes.

The essential oil constitutes 2.5 to 5% of the dry weight of the cumin fruits. The oil includes alcohols (2 to 5%), mostly aldehydes and ketones (50 to 70%), hydrocarbons (30 to 50%) and ethers (less than 1%). The distinctive and pungent odour and taste probably derive from dihydrocuminaldehyde and monoterpenes.

close-up of dried cumin fruits

Traditional medicine uses the fruits in mixtures as an astringent, a stimulant, and a stomachic and also for treating colic and diarrhoea. In Peninsular Malaysian folk medicine, the fruit is often pounded together with the leaves of other species to make a poultice for various diseases. The essential oil from cumin is used as a light anaesthetic, antispasmodic, aphrodisiac, carminative, diuretic, emmenagogue, fungicide, and insecticide and as veterinary medication. Ethiopians apply a paste of the pounded leaves to treat skin diseases.

Storage:
The fruits can be stored in an airtight bottle for long periods in a cool and dry place.

In Thai Dishes:
The standard proportion in curry pastes is two parts coriander to one part cumin seeds. Cumin is also used in meat and poultry curries. It is an important spice component in Muslim curries.

Curries
gaeng gai heng (chicken curry
with holy basil, ginger and peanuts)
gaeng kari pet (aromatic duck in yellow curry)
gaeng keo wan loogchin pla/koong (Thai green curry
with fish/prawn dumplings)
gaeng mussaman (Muslim curry)
gaeng muu phrik thai orn (pork and
green peppercorn curry)
gaeng phet taet (hot and sour prawn
and cucumber curry)
gaeng taeng muu gap nor mai (red curry of pork
and bamboo shoots)
khao soi (curry noodles from the Tai people,
an ethnic group living in southern China,
parts of Indochina and South Asia)
phrik gaeng (Thai curry pastes)

Other Dishes
khao mok gai (Muslim dish of chicken braised
in rice with turmeric and spices)
peanut sauce for *satay* (Thai recipe)

NOTES
Cumin is often confused with the caraway (*Carum carvi* L.). Both come from the same family and do look alike, but caraway plants are much larger and their fruits are more curved than the cumin. The best way to make a distinction between the two is to taste the seeds.

turmeric rhizomes

Turmeric

Scientific or botanical name:
Curcuma longa

Synonyms:
Amomum curcuma,
Curcuma domestica

**Scientific or botanical
name of family:**
Zingiberaceae

Common names:
English: turmeric, curcuma,
Indian saffron, long-rooted curcuma,
yellow ginger
Thai: *khamin* (general),
khamin-kaeng (northern Thailand),
khamin-chan (central Thailand),
khamin-hua (Chiang Mai)

Common family name:
ginger family

*side view and cross-sections of
cut rhizome*

Botanical Description:

This plant is a typical member of the ginger family, being a perennial plant which has a rhizome that has erect, leafy shoots. The rhizome, is a fleshy, branched, orange structure which somewhat resembles a cactus plant. Each part of the rhizome is ringed by the leaf scars of fallen leaves. Branches may range from 5 to 10 cm in length by 1 to 1.5 cm in diameter. The tough, thread-like roots grow from the rhizome and their tips often have an ellipsoidal tuber. At the branch tips is the pseudostem which consists of several overlapping cylindrical leaf bases. The outer leaves consist only of the cylindrical sheath. Further in, each leaf consists of a cylindrical leaf base, leaf stalk and a leaf blade. Each pseudostem contains up to about 10 leaves with blades that are half-oblong, half-lanceolate, and 7 to 70 cm long by 3 to 18 cm wide. The inflorescence grows at the tip of a central pseudostem and consists of many spirally arranged bracts below the white to yellowish white flowers, all of which form a cylindrical structure. No fruits are produced in this species.

Uses:

The main use of this species is the rhizome, which is used as a culinary spice, especially as a main constituent in curry powders for Asian dishes. Fresh young rhizomes and shoots may be eaten as a vegetable. The ground rhizome is used as a colouring agent in confectionery, textile dyes, pharmaceuticals and processed foods. It is also used as a cheaper but excellent saffron substitute (in this case, white rice is coloured and flavoured with the turmeric). Turmeric oil and turmeric oleoresin have similar applications as the ground rhizome.

Rhizomes are used in cosmetics as well as in traditional medicine as a blood 'purifier', a cure for the common cold or skin infections, in treating purulent ophthalmia, and as a stomachic and tonic. Rhizome extracts can also kill fungi, insects and nematodes.

side view and longitudinal section of rhizome

The rhizome yields 2 to 7% essential oil from steam distillation. The orange-red and slightly fluorescent oil consists of arturmerone, termerone and zingiberene. When extracted with ethanol or organic solvents such as acetone, the rhizome yields 6 to 10% oleoresin which partly consists of curcumin and its derivatives.

Curcumin has been reported to reduce the action of some genes promoting inflammation that is associated with colon cancer, heart disease and Alzheimer's disease.

Storage:
This spice is best used freshly purchased from the market. Clean the rhizome, blot dry with paper towels and then wrap in dry paper towels in the vegetable crisper of the refrigerator. It should last at least a week. Commercially, to improve the colour and enhance the fragrance, the cleaned rhizomes are boiled for an hour in slightly alkaline water, dried in the sun or by hot-air dryers for about a week and polished to smoothen their surface.

In Thai Dishes:
Turmeric is used primarily in Arab-influenced dishes such as *mussaman* (Muslim) curries and aromatic rice dishes that are cooked with several different spices at once. It is occasionally eaten raw by the Thais and can have a very intense flavour. The powder (or the rhizome sliced very thinly) is commonly used in curries. It is a good marinade for fish as it counteracts the fishiness. Turmeric is commonly used in southern Thai cooking.

Curry Pastes
phrik gaeng (Thai curry pastes, especially the *nahm phrik gaeng kari*, or yellow curry paste)

Fish Dishes
pla doog phat pet ka-min (fried catfish with chilli and turmeric)
pla jian (fish with ginger sauce)
pla thod patani (Patani fried fish)
tom gati pla grapong taeng (Red Emperor snapper, turmeric and coconut soup)
tom kem kati pla doog (catfish in turmeric sauce)

Other Dishes
gai yang (barbecued or grilled chicken)
gluay yang kamin (grilled bananas with coconut cream and turmeric)
khao buri ('city' rice)

NOTES
The common name of this spice is frequently misspelled and mispronounced as 'tumeric' (too-meric) rather than 'turmeric' (ter-meric). The scientific name of *Curcuma longa* is now generally accepted after a long debate.

turmeric plants in front, side and oblique views

lemon grass plant

Scientific or botanical name:
Cymbopogon citratus

Synonyms:
Andropogon citratus, Andropogon ceriferus, Andropogon nardus var. *ceriferus*

Scientific or botanical name of family:
Gramineae or Poaceae

Common names:
English: lemon grass, citronella grass, West Indian lemon grass
Thai: *cha khrai* (northern Thailand), *khrai* (Peninsular Thailand)

Common family name:
grass family

Lemon grass

Botanical Description:
This is a large tufted grass, usually about 0.7 to 1 m tall but can reach up to 3 m. There is a weakly branched rhizome at or just below soil level, from which many short erect stems develop. These stems bear many leaves, each consisting (from bottom up) of a leathery, cylindrical sheath and a long, narrow leaf blade 50 to 100 cm long by 0.5 to 2 cm wide. The leaf blades are pointed at the tips, waxy, light green and sharp to the touch because they contain silica cells in the outermost cell layer. (Note: do not pull on the leaves with your bare hands because the silica cells, which are as sharp as glass, will cut your hands.) The inflorescence grows up to 60 cm long and consists of many tiny flowers. Fruits are cylindrical to somewhat round but rarely develop from the flowers.

Uses:
The young erect stem, together with the leaf bases, is used in Thai cooking. Since the essential oil which produces the desired aroma is found mainly in the leaf bases, the leaves have most of their leaf blades trimmed off to

bottom of plant showing leaf sheaths

make them more compact when used. This species is cultivated in home gardens in Southeast Asia for cooking spicy sauces and curries or in making sherbet. The young stems are sometimes eaten with rice.

Currently, the leaves and stems of lemon grass are used as a source of essential oil and as a condiment. The oil, consisting mainly of citral, is used in the manufacture of other compounds used for perfumes. Citral is a mixture of geranial (40 to 62%) and neral (25 to 38%), plus smaller amounts of myrcene, limonene and geraniol. The oil is also used in food products, including beverages.

This plant is excellent for controlling soil erosion because its roots can bind soil effectively on bunds. It can also be used for mulch.

Lemon grass has medicinal properties and is used as a carminative or anticholeric and also in traditional medicine for the treatment of intestinal problems, eczema, colds, headaches, stomachaches, abdominal pains and rheumatic pains. Ticks in cattle and external parasites that live on chickens can be controlled by applying lemon grass oil. The oil also has antibacterial and antifungal properties.

Storage:

The portion of the short stem that is enclosed by the leaf sheaths is best stored wrapped in paper towels and kept in the refrigerator's vegetable crisper where it should last at least a week. Interestingly, the oil in the leaves may be detected even after long periods. (Specimens have even been found in 3000-year-old Egyptian tombs.) If the climate is suitable, this very hardy and trouble-free plant may be grown in your garden so fresh stems are available all the time.

In Thai Dishes:

The lemon-scented grass is very important in Thai cooking. Only the bottom part of the plant or the fleshy leave bases is used, bruised and left to boil in curries and soups or sliced and sprinkled in tangy salads.

longitudinal section of the plant showing stem and leaf bases

Curries and Sauces
gaeng keo wan (Thai green curry)
phrik gaeng (Thai curry pastes)

Salads
nahm phrik takrai (prawn and lemon grass relish)
yam ta-krai (lemon grass salad)

Soups
tom kha gai (spicy chicken, galangal
and coconut milk soup)
tom kha phak (vegetable, galangal
and coconut milk soup)
tom yam het (hot and sour mushroom soup)
tom yam koong (hot and sour prawn soup)
tom yam talay (hot and sour seafood soup)

Other Dishes
gai tung (spicy braised chicken)
gai yang (barbecued or grilled chicken)
pla thod patani (Patani fried fish)

NOTES

Many of the 55 species in the genus *Cymbopogon* yield lemon grass oil. Besides *Cymbopogon citratus*, the other important species are East Indian lemon grass (*Cymbopogon flexuosus*) and Jammu lemon grass (*Cymbopogon pendulus*).

Cardamom

Scientific or botanical name:
Elettaria cardamomum

Synonyms:
Amomum cardamomum, Amomum repents, Alpinia cardamomum

Scientific or botanical name of family:
Zingiberaceae

Common names:
English: cardamom, bastard cardamom, cardamom seed, Ceylon cardamom, cluster cardamom, lesser cardamom, Malabar cardamom, round cardamom, small cardamom, true cardamom
Thai: *krawan-thet* (central Thailand), *luk kravan* (general)

Common family name:
ginger family

dried cardamom fruits

Botanical Description:

This plant is a typical member of the ginger family, being a perennial plant that has a rhizome. The rhizome develops erect shoots which bear leaves. The rhizome grows at or just below soil level and produces about 10 to 20 pseudostems that consist primarily of several overlapping leaf sheaths. Each leaf has, from bottom up, a leaf sheath, leaf stalk and lanceolate leaf blade, 25 to 100 cm long by 5 to 15 cm wide. The leaf is dark green above and light green and hairy or hairless on the underside. Usually prostrate, the inflorescence extends to 1.2 m, arising from the rhizome at the base of a pseudostem. Each joint of the inflorescence has a bract which has in its angle a short shoot of two to three flowers which are about 4 cm long. The sepals are light green and the petals mostly white. The fruit is a round or tri-lobed capsule usually 1 to 2 cm long, but occasionally reaching 5 cm. The 3 mm, dark brown, aromatic seeds range from 15 to 20 per fruit. When fresh, they are covered with mucilage.

top, side and bottom views of fruit

dried fruit dissected to show fruit wall, seed clusters, individual seeds and central axis

Uses:

The whole dried fruit is used as a spice for home cooking. In Asian cooking, this spice is used in a range of rice dishes, as well as meat and vegetable or curry dishes. It is also used to flavour beverages such as coffee and tea, in baked goods and confectioneries, and in savoury dishes in the food industry. It is sometimes used to flavour tobacco and as a masticatory in betel quid.

Cardamom is considered a carminative, diuretic, laxative, stomachic and tonic for the heart. It is also used to reduce inflammation, earache, headache and toothache as well as alleviate disorders of the chest, liver and throat.

Cardamom essential oil is used in flavouring processed foods, cordials, bitters and liqueurs and in perfumes. The essential oil content of the dried fruit is 3.5 to 7% and is best obtained by steam distillation. The essential oil consists of 1,8-cineole (20 to 60%) and α-terpinyl acetate (20 to 53%) with minor quantities of other oxygenated monoterpenes, monoterpene hydrocarbons and sequiterpenes. Cardamomum oleoresin has similar usage as the essential oil.

Storage:

The dried fruits are best kept in a cool and dry place in a sealed container to prevent insect and fungal attack.

In Thai Dishes:

Cardamon is not commonly used in Thai dishes, but one can find it in the *mussaman* (Muslim) curries of supposed Persian origins or in the aromatic rice dish, *khao buri* ('city' rice), thought to be a dish adopted from the Arab traders who plied the Arab-Chinese trade routes.

Dishes

gaeng mussaman gai (Muslim curry with chicken)
khao buri ('city' rice)
khao mok gai (Muslim dish of chicken braised in rice with turmeric and spices)
muu thod kreuangthet (deep-fried pork with spices)
peanut sauce for *satay* (Thai recipe)

NOTES

The common name 'cardamom' is often also applied to species in the genera *Afromomum*, *Alpinia* or *Amomum*, which are substitutes of *Elattaria cardomomum*, such as Korarima cardamom (*Aframomum corrorima*), round cardamon (*Amomum compactum*) or Chinese cardamon (*Alpinia globosa*).

four different side views and dried fruit with one part of the fruit wall opened to show seeds inside

Scientific or botanical name:
Eryngium foetidum

Synonym:
Eryngium antihystericum

Scientific or botanical name of family:
Apiaceae or Umbelliferae

Common Names:
English: sawtooth coriander, spiny coriander, Mexican coriander
Thai: *hom-pomkula* (northern Thailand), *mae-lae-doe* (northern Thailand), *phakchi-farang* (central Thailand)

Common family name:
celery family

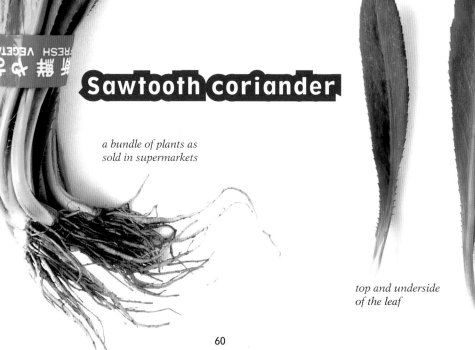

Sawtooth coriander

a bundle of plants as sold in supermarkets

top and underside of the leaf

close-up of inflorescence, with flowers in tiny compact clusters

Botanical Description:

An erect, perennial herb up to 80 cm tall, the sawtooth coriander has a distinct taproot. In young plants, the leaves are clustered into a rosette at the base of the stem which elongates before it produces flowers at the branching tip. The leaves are stalkless to shortly stalked, with the blade quite narrow but wider in the upper half, 5 to 32 cm long by 1 to 4 cm wide, with a spiny-toothed margin. The leaves produce an unpleasant scent when bruised. The inflorescence has two bracts at each branch and bears many tiny, light green flowers. The fruit grows up to 1.5 mm long by 0.75 mm wide and splits into two parts when ripe.

Uses:

The aromatic leaves, which smell like those of coriander, are used fresh to flavour curries, rice and fish dishes, soups and stews. The tender, young, fresh (or cooked) leaves are eaten as a vegetable. The essential oils, obtained by steam distillation of the leaves and roots, consist mostly of aldehydes and some monoterpene hydrocarbons. The aldehydes consist mostly of alkanals and alkenals and are thought to be responsible for the strong aroma of the plant.

A decoction of the root has been used medicinally as an antipyretic, a diuretic, a stimulant or a sudorific, whereas the decoction or juice of the leaves has been used as an antipyretic, a cure for colds, a laxative and a stimulant. The decoction of the whole plant is used to treat high blood pressure, and as an abortifacient, aphrodisiac and emmenagogue.

Storage:

The whole plant is sold in markets as it is best used fresh. To store newly purchased plants, rinse the plant in running tap water to remove the soil particles. Allow it

to dry out or blot it dry with paper towels, then wrap it in dry paper towels before putting it in a plastic bag and storing this in the vegetable crisper of the refrigerator.

In Thai Dishes:

Used mainly in salads, sawtooth coriander is shredded and one to two tablespoons are added. It is less intense than coriander and is used in warm salads as the fragrance is released mostly when it is warm.

Salads
laab gai (northeastern chicken salad
with mint and lemon grass)
yam gop gati tian (coconut chicken salad)
yam het bpa (wild mushroom salad)
yam hoi nang rom (oyster salad)

Soups
tom gai maprao pao (spicy chicken soup
with cooked coconut)

NOTES

Substitutes for this species include coriander (*Coriandrum sativum*), Vietnamese coriander (*Persicaria odorata*) and other *Eryngium* species.

*sawtooth
coriander plants*

*margins of the
leaf blade*

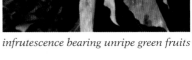

infrutescence bearing unripe green fruits

*tip, cross-section
and bottom of young
inflorescence*

*longitudinal section and
side view of young inflorescence*

Torch ginger

Scientific or botanical name:
Etlingera elatior

Synonyms:
*Alpinia elatior, Nicolaia speciosa,
Phaeomeria speciosa*

**Scientific or botanical
name of family:**
Zingiberaceae

Common names:
English: torch ginger, ginger
bud, Javanese aromatic ginger,
Indonesian tall ginger, pink ginger
bud, Nicola flower buds,
Philippine waxflower
Thai: *kaalaa* (general)

Common family name:
ginger family

mature torch ginger inflorescence with dead flowers below and opened flowers (with yellow-fringed scarlet petals) at the middle and unopened flowers (buds) above

inflorescence just beginning to bloom with lower bracts unfurling and lowermost flowers opened

Botanical Description:

A tall and free-flowering plant, the main stem consists of a thick, horizontally-growing rhizome. From the rhizome arise a few vertical pseudostems. These are actually many leaves whose sheaths wrap around each other tightly. These pseudostems may be 2.5 to 5 m tall. The leaf blades are borne in two distinct rows along this axis. The inflorescence or flowering shoot arises vertically from the rhizome, apparently from the ground, rising from 0.5 to 2.5 m tall. The young inflorescence consists of a narrow, light green, cylindrical stalk which bears a spindle-shaped tip consisting of light pink bracts tightly wrapped around each other. The flower buds are found within the bracts, and the flowers have mostly pink petals up to 4 cm long, one of which is slightly longer, deep crimson and white- or yellow-edged. The single stamen in the flower is 2.5 cm long and consists of a red anther and white filament. The stigma is dark red, club-shaped and borne on a thin, red style which is hairy near its tip. The flowers develop into fruits which are found in a somewhat spherical structure. The berry-like fruits, when ripe, are red and 2 to 2.5 cm in diameter.

Uses:

The pleasantly and subtly fragrant bracts of the young inflorescence (with the flowers not yet emerged) are primarily used as a flavouring ingredient in curries and mixed vegetables or eaten fresh. In Southeast Asia, the inflorescences are grown mostly in home gardens or semi-managed in groves in secondary forests and thus only available fresh at local markets.

Forty-five compounds have been identified in the essential oil of the young inflorescences, which is obtained through steam distillation. The main components are aliphatic alcohols, aliphatic aldehydes and terpenoids.

Storage:

Wrap the whole inflorescence in a dry paper towel and secure this with a rubber band. Then place this in the vegetable crisper of a refrigerator where it should last up to a week. If kept longer, it will dry up. When a portion of an inflorescence has been used, store the remainder in an airtight plastic food container which has been sprinkled with a little tap water to increase the relative humidity inside the container. Store this in the refrigerator.

In Thai Dishes:

The raw young inflorescence is added to the popular southern Thai rice salad, *khao yam*, or eaten raw together with a spicy dip.

NOTES

The species is also grown as an ornamental plant in semi-shaded areas because of the rather neat appearance of the leaves and the very attractive inflorescence which, when fully opened, resembles a bright pink, many-petalled lotus flower.

inflorescence just beginning to bloom

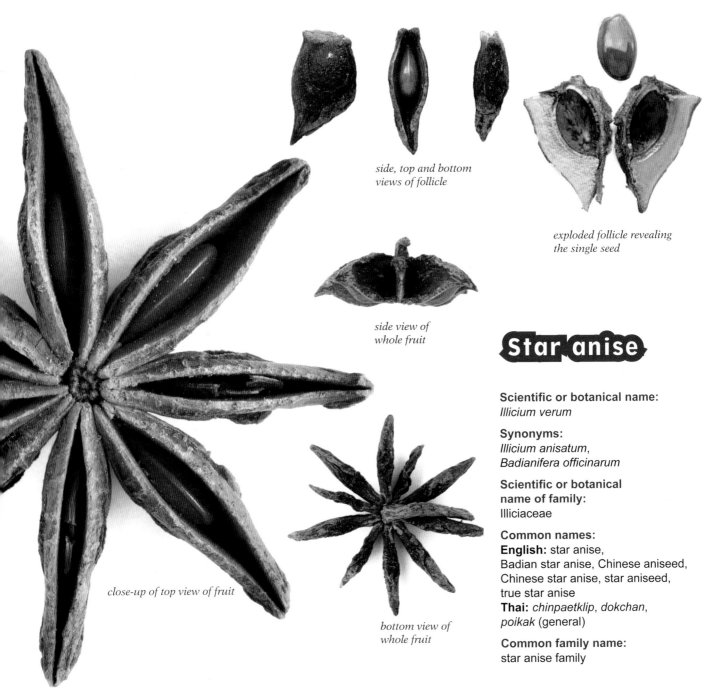

side, top and bottom
views of follicle

exploded follicle revealing
the single seed

side view of
whole fruit

close-up of top view of fruit

bottom view of
whole fruit

Star anise

Scientific or botanical name:
Illicium verum

Synonyms:
Illicium anisatum,
Badianifera officinarum

**Scientific or botanical
name of family:**
Illiciaceae

Common names:
English: star anise,
Badian star anise, Chinese aniseed,
Chinese star anise, star aniseed,
true star anise
Thai: *chinpaetklip*, *dokchan*,
poikak (general)

Common family name:
star anise family

Botanical Description:

The tree is a tall evergreen that grows up to a height of 20 m. The leathery leaves are simple, alternately arranged along the branches and elliptical in shape. Individual flowers are borne in the axils of the branch and leaf stalk. The flowers, which are 1 to 1.5 cm in diameter, vary in colour from very light pink to red to greenish yellow. The reddish brown fruit is distinctive and consists of about eight woody, boat-shaped follicles arranged around a central axis, giving rise to the common name 'star anise'. Each follicle contains one seed.

Uses:

The ripe fruit of the Chinese star anise is used in flavouring curries, soups and rice and also in medicine. An essential oil, made up chiefly of trans-anethole (70 to 93%), is extracted from the fruits, leaves and twigs by steam distillation. The oil is a primary flavouring agent in liqueurs, chewing gum, sweets, baked goods and meat products. It is also used as a scent in soaps, tobacco and dental cream.

As a traditional medicine, the powder of the fruits is used to treat abdominal colic, lumbago, gastric pains and diarrhoea. It is also included in a compound as an emmenagogue. The fruit has oestrogenic properties and is used to promote, aside from menstruation, milk secretion as well as increase male libido. As an essential oil, it has stimulatory properties and can be used to alleviate rheumatism and repel body lice and bed bugs. The oil is also used in the manufacture of perfumes and synthetic oestrogens.

Storage:

It is best to store the fruits in an airtight container placed in a cool, dry place to prevent loss of the essential oil that gives it its aroma.

In Thai Dishes:

The sweet liquorice-like aroma of the star anise is said to enhance the appetite. The spice is not commonly used in Thai cooking. However the *parlow*, a soup originating from China, is common in Thai food markets where the sweet smell of the star anise wafts through the air.

Dishes
gaeng hang lae (northern pork curry)
kai parlow (braised quail eggs with star anise)
muu grop warn (sweet and fried crispy pork)
muu parlow (pork braised with star anise)
muu sorng yang (pork cooked in two styles)

NOTES

The Chinese star anise is often confused with other species of *Illicium* on account of the star-shaped fruits. This is dangerous as *Illicium anisatum* L. (the Japanese star anise, also called *Illicium religiosum*) has poisonous fruits, with shikimine as a constituent, which is used as an insecticide and sold in herbal medicines to treat toothache and dermatitis. The poisonous species of *Illicium anisatum* has smaller fruits and does not form a regular star due to the abortion of some of the carpels, and its follicles are more wrinkled and more sharply pointed at the apex. It is important to use the proper scientific name to distinguish the two or use 'Chinese star anise' for *Illicium verum* and 'Japanese star anise' for *Illicium anisatum*. The two can also be distinguished by taste. The Japanese star anise has a balsamic odour and a disagreeable bitterness.

Pimpinella anisum L., the anise, also has anethole as a major essential oil component and competes with Chinese star anise commercially because they may be substituted for each other.

leafy branch tip

*leafy branch
with flowers*

Bay leaf

Scientific or botanical name:
Laurus nobilis

Synonym:
Laurus undulata

**Scientific or botanical
name of family:**
Lauraceae

Common names:
English: Bay leaf, laurel,
sweet bay tree
Thai: *bai ka wan*

Common family name:
laurel family

Botanical Description:

This aromatic tree can grow to a height of 15 m. When in cultivation, it is usually pruned to a shrub of a few metres tall. The trunk bark is blackish brown. The simple leaves are arranged alternately along the branches and the leaf blades are oblong-elliptical, rough to touch and have distinctive undulating margins. The leaf blades are dark green above, pale green on the underside and dotted with many tiny glands. Ten to 12 pairs of lateral veins are visible on both sides of the leaves. A few yellowish green flowers are clustered in an umbel and found in the axil of the leaf stalk and the branch. The fruit, shaped like an olive, grows to 2 cm long and is a glossy black when mature.

Uses:

Bay leaves are used to impart flavour to all kinds of meats, fish dishes, sauces, stocks and stews. The fruits are also used, to a lesser extent, for similar purposes. The crushed leaves are an essential ingredient in mixed pickling spices and are used on an industrial scale in meat products, in making vinegar and in pastries.

The leaves are added early in the cooking as the taste intensifies gradually. They should be removed from the dish after cooking as they have sharp edges and can cause internal injuries when ingested.

The laurel has a long history as a medicinal plant. The leaves and berries are astringent, stomachic, stimulant and narcotic. A decoction of the leaves is used to treat urinary problems and dropsy and is said to be a powerful emmenagogue. The seed oil is useful in treating rheumatic pains.

The essential oil of laurel leaves consists of 140 components, with 1,8-cineole making up as much as 50%. The oil is colourless and strongly aromatic with a warm, fresh and penetrating camphor-like odour that resembles eucalyptus leaves. The flavour is peppery, medicinal, and sweet and has a bitter aftertaste.

Storage:

Fresh leaves are bitter while old dried leaves are considered poor, so the best leaves are those that have been dried for just a few days. Dried leaves purchased from the supermarket should be kept sealed in a re-sealable plastic bag and placed in a cool, dry place.

In Thai Dishes:

Bay leaves are seldom used in Thai cuisine and feature mostly in dishes of Arab influence such as the *mussaman* (Muslim) curries and the *khao buri* ('city' rice).

Dishes
gaeng mussaman gai (Muslim curry with chicken)
khao buri ('city' rice)
khao mok gai (Muslim dish of chicken braised in rice with turmeric and spices)

NOTES

In classical Greece, wreaths made of laurel leaves were used to honour heroes and poets. The words 'laureate' and 'baccalaureaus' are derived from the word 'laurel'.

top and underside of leaf

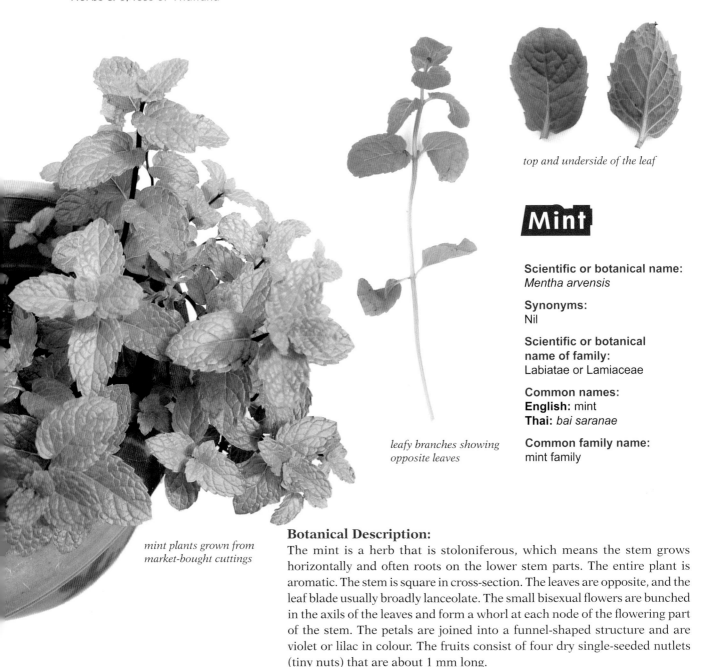

top and underside of the leaf

Mint

Scientific or botanical name:
Mentha arvensis

Synonyms:
Nil

Scientific or botanical name of family:
Labiatae or Lamiaceae

Common names:
English: mint
Thai: *bai saranae*

Common family name:
mint family

leafy branches showing opposite leaves

mint plants grown from market-bought cuttings

Botanical Description:

The mint is a herb that is stoloniferous, which means the stem grows horizontally and often roots on the lower stem parts. The entire plant is aromatic. The stem is square in cross-section. The leaves are opposite, and the leaf blade usually broadly lanceolate. The small bisexual flowers are bunched in the axils of the leaves and form a whorl at each node of the flowering part of the stem. The petals are joined into a funnel-shaped structure and are violet or lilac in colour. The fruits consist of four dry single-seeded nutlets (tiny nuts) that are about 1 mm long.

Uses:

The fresh fragrant leaves are used mainly as a condiment. The characteristic cool taste of the leaves is due to menthol which is a monoterpenoid alcohol. The most important use of mint is its oil and this is produced on a global scale. In the period 1990 to 1995, the production of mint from the Japanese cultivar generated US$43 million per year on average, based on 4,000 to 4,500 tonnes per year. The oil is used medicinally in ointments, itch-relief creams, cough syrups, lozenges and tablets and as a flavouring agent in toothpaste, mouthwash, chewing gum, beverages, confectionery, cigarettes, etc. In the perfume industry, it is used in soaps and shampoos.

All over the world, the mint leaf and its oil have wide medicinal applications. It is an antispasmodic, astringent, carminative, emmenagogue, sedative, stimulant, stomachic, sudorific and frigerant.

In Thailand especially, the mint leaf is a widely featured culinary herb.

Storage:

The leaves should ideally be bought fresh and used immediately. For short-term storage, the leaves are best stored wrapped in paper towels in the refrigerator's vegetable crisper where they should keep for at least a week. The plant is easy to grow and proliferates so if it is cultivated in the kitchen garden, leaves can be available fresh anytime.

In Thai Dishes:

Mint is used mostly in salads and is used generously in combination with coriander or basil leaves as a garnish. Do not cut the mint with a knife or the leaves will blacken (just like basil). It is better to tear it. The menthol flavour is a cool antidote to the usually fiery and sour Thai salads.

Mint leaves are commonly used as a garnish in imaginative Thai desserts such as the *See Da Ram Dong* ('The Faithful See Da'). This dish derives from an episode of the *Ramakein*, the Thai version of the *Ramayana*, a Hindu epic. See Da (Sita), the wife of Phra Ram (Rama), was captured by the Monkey King but resisted the seductions of her captor and remained true (*ram dong*) to her husband. The *Ramayana* teaches the moral lessons which are part and parcel of Buddhist and Hindu culture. The dessert in question is made with peeled bananas, unsweetened coconut cream, sugar, orange extract, vanilla ice-cream and fresh mint leaves as a garnish. The white of the banana and the coconut cream are symbols of See Da's purity and faithfulness.

Desserts
khao neuw khao poud (sweet glutinous rice
with corn)
See Da Ram Dong ('The Faithful See Da')

Salads
laab gai (northeastern chicken salad
with mint and lemon grass)
laab muu (northeastern pork salad
with mint and lemon grass)
laab neua (northeastern beef salad
with mint and lemon grass)
nahm tok (grilled beef salad)
sup nor mai (northeastern shredded bamboo salad)
yam gai yang (grilled chicken salad)
yam gung mung gorn (grilled lobster salad)
yam hoy nang rom (oyster salad)
yam koong sawan ('heavenly' prawn salad)
yam nang muu (pork rind with lemon grass salad)
yam pla muk (squid salad)
yam yai (Thai chef's salad)

NOTES

There is pharmacological evidence supporting the traditional use of mint as a carminative and stomachic. In experiments, the oil has been shown to cure ringworm in guinea pigs within two weeks. The oil also shows antibacterial activity against *Listeria* and *Salmonella* species. However, high doses of mint oil can be toxic.

Nutmeg

longitudinal sections, cross-sections and side views of dried kernels

young tree

Scientific or botanical name:
Myristica fragrans

Synonyms:
Myristica officinalis, Myristica moschata, Myristica aromatica

Scientific or botanical name of family:
Myristicaceae

Common names:
English: nutmeg, mace, nutmeg tree
Thai: *chan-ban* (northern Thailand), *look chan*, *dok chan* or *chan-thet* (central Thailand)

Common family name:
nutmeg family

Botanical Description:

This is a tree 5 to 13 m tall. The bark exudes a sticky red sap when cut. All parts of the plant are aromatic. The alternate, stalked leaves have elliptical leaf blades which are smooth, thin and papery. The tree is unisexual, whereby male and female flowers are found on separate trees. The flowers are cup-shaped and small, and males have more flowers per cluster. The fruit is fleshy and yellowish and resembles a large apricot. It splits into two fleshy halves upon ripening to reveal a red aril, a waxy mace networked around a stony hard dark brown seed. The mace used in commerce is the dried aril and the nutmeg is the dried kernel of the seed. The mace is the more expensive of the two.

Uses:

The dry, shelled seed (nutmeg) and the dried aril (mace), ground or whole, are used to flavour processed foods. Domestic culinary use actually accounts for more of the major demand for ground mace, where it is used to flavour meats, soups and stews. Ground nutmeg is preferred in sweet dishes while ground mace is said to be more suitable for savoury dishes. It is also used to flavour milk. The nutmeg is said to have astringent, carminative, stimulative and aphrodisiac properties.

The essential oils are made up of monoterpene hydrocarbons, oxygenated monoterpenes and aromatic ethers of myristicin, elemicin and safrole. The oils can be used as insecticides, fungicides and bactericides.

top and underside of the leaf

part of the aril (mace) of a nutmeg seed

The oil is used in flavouring food products, liqueurs, soft drinks, perfumes (often men's perfume formulations) and soaps. It is also used in pharmaceutical formulations to treat bronchial problems. The important extracts of nutmeg and mace are the oleoresins and these possess a truer flavour and odour than the essential oils.

Owing to its myristicin and elemicin content, nutmeg can be used as a narcotic. Powdered nutmeg has been occasionally used dangerously as a hallucinogenic drug. Consumption of 8 g of pure nutmeg is said to be lethal, because of the myristicin and elemicin content. The husk (pericarps) can be made into sweetmeats, jellies, marmalades and sweets which are popular in Southeast Asia.

Storage:

The oils are volatile and the dried mace and nutmeg should be kept in an airtight container in a cool, dry place.

In Thai Dishes:

Powdered nutmeg is recommended for curries to increase the flavour. Some recipes make the distinction between nutmeg and mace.

Curries and Pastes

gaeng gai heng (chicken curry with holy basil ginger
and peanuts, using mace)
gaeng kari gai (aromatic chicken in yellow curry,
using nutmeg)
gaeng kari pet (aromatic duck in yellow curry,
using mace)
gaeng keo wan (Thai green curry, using nutmeg)
gaeng mussaman (Muslim curries,
using mace and nutmeg)
gaeng panaeng (Thai Penang curry pastes,
using nutmeg)
gaeng phet daeng (Thai red curry, using nutmeg)
gaeng phet taet (hot and sour prawn and cucumber
curry, using nutmeg)

Other Dishes

khao buri ('city' rice, using mace and nutmeg)
khao soy (curry noodles from the Tai people, an ethnic
group living in southern China, parts of Indochina
and South Asia, using nutmeg and mace)
muu thod kreuangthet (deep-fried pork
with spices, using nutmeg)
peanut sauce for *satay* (Thai recipe, using nutmeg)

*seed with and
without aril*

NOTES

There has been an ongoing search for techniques to sex the seeds or seedlings at an early stage as these plants are unisexual and there is economic loss in planting excess male plants (since they bear no fruit and seed). One old belief was to feed the fruits to pigeons in hope that the sex of the pigeon that ate and excreted the seed would then determine the sex of the tree. These days, more advanced methods investigating the sex chromosomes are being tested. However, the chromosomes are very small (0.4 to 1 micrometre) and this technique is evidently hard to inculcate in the cultivation of the nutmeg.

*male flower's top and
side views, with perianth
partially removed to show
the stamens which are fused
together into a tube-like
structure and half-flower*

fruiting branch

leafy branch bundle of sweet basil as sold in supermarkets

Basils

Scientific or botanical names:
Ocimum americanum
Ocimum basilicum
Ocimum tenuiflorum

Synonyms:
For *Ocimum americanum*: *Ocimum africanum, Ocimum brachiatum, Ocimum canum*

For *Ocimum basilicum*: Nil

For *Ocimum tenuiflorum*: *Ocimum brachiatum, Ocimum flexuosum, Ocimum sanctum*

Scientific or botanical name of family:
Labiatae or Lamiaceae

Common names:
For *Ocimum americanum*
English: American basil, hoary basil, lemon basil, lime basil, Thai basil, Thai lemon basil
Thai: *maenglak* (central Thailand), *kom ko khao* (northern Thailand), *tu* (general)

For *Ocimum basilicum*
English: basil, common basil, garden basil, Roman basil, sweet basil, Thai basil
Thai: *horapha*

For *Ocimum tenuiflorum*
English: holy basil, monk's basil, red basil, rough basil, sacred basil, sacred Thai basil, Siamese basil, Thai basil
Thai: *kaphrao, kaphrao daeng khon, kaphrao khon* (central Thailand), *kom ko dong* (Chiang Mai), *im-khim-lam* (northern Thailand)

Common family name:
mint family

78

Botanical Description:

All three *Ocimum* species are very aromatic herbs. The stems are square in cross-section and branch profusely. The stalked leaves are arranged in a decussate manner, where the arrangement of a pair of opposite leaves intersects the next to form a cross and so on. About 6 to 10 small flowers are arranged in whorls at the nodes of the inflorescence. Both the calyx and corolla are bell-shaped. The calyx has two lips and the upper lip is usually broad; the lower lip usually has four narrow pointed 'teeth'. The corolla also has two lips with a longer lower lip. There are two pairs of stamens and the style is forked. The fruit consists of nutlets enclosed in the mature calyx.

These three species are found in Southeast Asia and a few key morphological differences distinguish them from one another. The differences between the three species are shown in the table below. Other characteristics relating to shape and size tend to overlap.

Ocimum americanum (hoary basil, *maenglak*)	*Ocimum basilicum* (sweet basil, *horapha*)	*Ocimum tenuiflorum* (holy basil, *kaphrao*)
The lower lip of the calyx is not curved backwards.	The lower lip of the calyx is not curved backwards.	The lower lip of the calyx is curved backwards.
The flower stalk is shorter than the calyx (the flowers are almost stalkless) and bent upright and appressed against the inflorescence axis.	The flower stalk is shorter than the calyx, bent upright and appressed against the inflorescence axis.	The pedicel is as long as the calyx and almost transverse to the inflorescence axis.
The corolla is 5 to 6 mm long and white.	The corolla is 7 to 9 mm long and white or violet.	The corolla is 3.5 to 4 mm long and lavender or white.
The fruiting calyx measures 4 to 6 mm long.	The fruiting calyx measures 5 to 9 mm long.	The fruiting calyx measures 3 to 3.5 mm long.
The scent of a crushed leaf is somewhat like lemon grass or lemony.	The scent of a crushed leaf is strongly minty.	The scent of a crushed leaf is mildly minty-grassy.
This species is considered very much similar in morphology to *Ocimum basilicum*, except that it is a slightly smaller-flowered wild form and a little hairier.	This species differs very little from *Ocimum americanum*. However, the chromosome numbers for the two species are different.	The main character that distinguishes this species from the other two *Ocimum* species is the flower stalk that is situated transverse to the main axis of the inflorescence. In *Ocimum basilicum*, the flower stalk is strongly bent backwards at the top.

*sweet basil, upper
portion of leafy shoot*

*top and underside
of sweet basil leaf*

*sweet basil
inflorescence
at branch tip*

Storage:
The leaves of basils are very delicate and bruise easily. They are best stored wrapped in paper towels in the vegetable crisper of the refrigerator. Growing a pot of the plant is strongly encouraged as the leaves are best used fresh.

Uses:
Ocimum americanum
This is used primarily as a vegetable and also as a flavouring for sauces, soups and salads. Medicinally, it is used as a mouthwash for relieving toothache.

Ocimum basilicum
This is a very popular savoury herb (certainly in Thai dishes). Sweet basil is cultivated throughout the world. Fresh leaves are normally used in cooking and the leaves should be added just before cooking is complete to retain their flavour. Medicinally, the sweet basil is a stimulant and carminative used to treat vomiting, coughs, chronic dysentery and diarrhoea. In Vietnam, the leaves are used to treat fever and malaria. The essential oil is used as a repellent against bugs and flies.

Ocimum tenuiflorum
This spice herb is sometimes used as a condiment in fruit and vegetable salads and other meat dishes. It is used more widely as a medicinal herb as it is thought to have antibacterial properties. The Indonesians use it to treat colds in children, heal wounds and promote lactation in women. It is also used to treat gonorrhoea (in the Philippines) and rheumatism (in Malaysia).

In Thai Dishes:
Three main types of basil are used in Thai cooking: the *maenglak* (hoary basil), the *horapha* (sweet basil) and the *kaphrao* (holy basil).

The *maenglak* is delicate, has a citrus fragrance, and is used in soups and salads and also in *khanom jin nam ya* (thin rice noodles with ground fish curry); it features most exclusively in *gaeng liang*, which is considered a primitive curry that uses *krachai* (Chinese keys) and *maenglak* as essential flavours together with ingredients such as freshwater fish or prawns. This dish is indigenous to the north and central plains.

The *horapha* has a heavy aniseed (seed of the anise) fragrance and liquorice flavour. It is used in curries, seafood dishes and *nahm phrik* relishes.

The *kaphrao* is reminiscent of cloves and is used in seafood dishes and hot and spicy stir-fries. The *kaphrao* and *horapha* are sometimes used as substitutes for each other, but the two basils taste completely different.

The leaves bruise black when cut with a knife (just like mint leaves) so it is best to tear the leaves instead.

Dishes

For *Ocimum americanum* (hoary basil, *maenglak*):
gaeng liang fak thong (spicy pumpkin soup)
gaeng liang pla (fish and vegetable curry with wild ginger, white pepper and lemon basil)
khanom jin nam ya (rice noodles with ground fish curry)
nahm ya pa (curry with no coconut milk, usually with milk)
(The tiny seeds of the *maenglak* develop a mucilaginous coat when soaked and resemble frogs' eggs. The soaked seeds are used as a garnish in cold desserts, syrupy drinks and have a nice crunch in the middle.)

For *Ocimum basilicum* (sweet basil, *horapha*):
gaeng keo wan (Thai green curry)
gaeng panaeng (Thai Penang curry)
gaeng pet muu yang kub klouy dipp (red curry with roast pork and green banana)
gaeng phet pet yang (roast duck in red curry sauce)
hoy malaeng puu bai horapha (mussels with sweet basil)
hoy mangpoo ob mor din (steamed mussels with lime leaves, galangal, or sweet basil)
pla bae sa (steamed fish with vermicelli and sweet basil)

top and underside of hoary basil leaf

hoary basil plant

hoary basil flowers

hoary basil inflorescence at stem tip

81

For *Ocimum tenuiflorum* (holy basil, *kaphrao*):
gaeng bpa pet (spicy duck curry without coconut milk)
gaeng gai heng (chicken curry with
holy basil ginger and peanuts)
gaeng kae nok pirap (curry of pigeon and herbs)
muu phat kraphao (fried spicy basil pork)
neua phat bau kraphao (stir-fried minced beef
with chilli and holy basil)
phat bai kraphrao (stir-fred meat with
chilli and holy basil)
phat kaphrao het (stir-fried mushrooms
with chilli and holy basil)
phat kraphao pet yang (stir-fried roast duck
with holy basil)
pla grop phat pet (stir-fried crispy fish
with holy basil and chilli)

*holy basil, young leaves and twig
showing characteristic hairiness*

*top and underside of
holy basil leaf*

holy basil inflorescence

leafy branch bundle of holy basil as sold in supermarkets

NOTES

Ocimum basilicum

This species was cultivated in Egypt as far back as 3,000 years ago. The major components of the essential oils of the leaves are methyl chavicol and linalool, although proportions of these may differ between varieties. The oil is antiseptic against Gram-positive and Gram-negative bacteria and also inhibits fungal activity. An alcohol extract of the leaves reportedly acts against HIV-1 (one of the viruses that causes AIDS).

The species has a very complex botanical relationship with other species of its genus and it is also very variable with at least seven varieties differentiated within the species itself. Some of the varieties are the results of crossing between other *Ocimum* species. *Ocimum americanum* and *Ocimum tenuiflorum*, which are found in Southeast Asia, are thought to be closely related.

Ocimum tenuiflorum

This is the most sacred plant in Hinduism, as it is a symbol of fidelity and pure divine love. It is grown as a sacred plant in homes, gardens and temples. It is only known from cultivation.

plant showing cut lower leaves

Scientific or botanical name:
Pandanus amaryllifolius

Synonyms:
Pandanus latifolius, Pandanus hasskarlii, Pandanus odorus

Scientific or botanical name of family:
Pandanaceae

Common names:
English: screwpine, fragrant screwpine, Indonesian screwpine, pandan, fragrant pandan, scented pandan
Thai: *bai-toey, bai toey-hom, panae-wo-nging, toey-hom* (general)

Common family name:
pandan family

leaf tip and cross-section showing lateral pleats

Botanical Description:
The plant consists of a stem bearing spirally arranged leaves, with aerial roots (prop roots) at the base of the stem and more roots growing into the ground at the bottom. The plants are usually short and not more than 1.5 m tall. The leaves are more or less stiff, linear and acute, measuring 30 to 60 cm in length. A characteristic of all pandan species is that the leaves are keeled beneath and have prominent twin lateral pleats above (to give an M-shaped cross-section). The margins of the leaves are spineless, unlike other *Pandanus* species which have very sharp spines along the margins of the leaves. The stem is stout and low-branching. Little is known of the flowers and fruits as the plant remains in a sterile state. There are two forms of this species: a smaller one whose leaves are used for their aroma, and a larger form, whose leaves are used for wrapping rice dumplings by the Chinese in Malaysia and Singapore. These leaves have a subtle flavour which is not as strong as that of the smaller form.

Uses:

Screwpine leaves are used throughout Southeast Asia in cooking. The fresh leaves impart that unmistakable aroma and green colouring (chlorophyll) to cakes, jellies, rice, sweets, etc. The leaves are used extensively in soups and desserts, especially those that involve coconut milk. It is thought that the fragrance comes not from the essential oil but from the oxidation and breakdown of a yellow pigment. The essential oil can be used as a repellent against cockroaches. Powdered leaves are used against the weevil (*Callosobruchus chinensis*), which infests mung beans.

In Thailand, the leaves are used as traditional medicine to treat diabetes. The infusions of the leaves are also used to treat restlessness. Coconut oil, in which screwpine leaves have been soaked, is used as an embrocation to treat rheumatism.

Storage:

To preserve the colour and the turgidity of the leaves, wrap them in wet paper towels and store in the vegetable crisper of the refrigerator. For long-term storage, one may consider freezing the leaves for use when needed (after thawing). Better yet, grow a pot of the plant at home from which leaves can be harvested fresh whenever they are needed.

In Thai Dishes:

Screwpine leaves are mainly used to flavour rice and desserts in Thai cuisine. It is used to make a sweet coconut cream (*gati lart naa khonom*) which is poured over desserts as a topping. The leaves are also used as a wrap in another Thai signature dish, *gai hor bai-toey* (Thai deep-fried chicken in screwpine leaf).

Desserts
gati lart naa khonom (coconut cream topping)
khao mun (rice cooked with coconut cream)
khao niaw guan (glutinous rice mixed with
sugar and coconut milk)

khonom chan bai-toey (layered cake
flavoured with screwpine)
khonom tom bai-toey (screwpine rice balls)
tar kor haew (tapioca and coconut pudding
with water chestnut)
wun bai-toey lae gati (screwpine and
coconut agar agar)

Other Dishes
gai hor bai-toey (deep-fried marinated chicken
in screwpine leaf)

NOTES

Pandanus amaryllifolius is the only *Pandanus* species with scented leaves. The origin of the fragrant screwpine is unknown and the plant has never been found wild. It is speculated to have originated either in India or the Moluccas (Indonesia).

larger form of the plant in cultivation

spikes of green peppercorns

white peppercorns

black peppercorns

Pepper

Scientific or botanical name:
Piper nigrum

Synonym:
Piper aromaticum

Scientific or botanical name of family:
Piperaceae

Common names:
English: pepper, black pepper, white pepper
Thai: *phrik-noi* (northern Thailand), *phrik-thai* (central Thailand)

Common family name:
pepper family

Botanical Description:

The pepper is a perennial woody climber that can grow up to 10 m or more. Grown on supports, they look more like cylindrical bushes. There are two types of growth forms in branches: the orthotropic branches are the ones that grow vertically and the plagiotropic ones are those that grow perpendicular to the main vertical axis. The orthotropic branches remain vegetative while the latter produce reproductive shoots. The leaves are arranged alternately. The stalked leaves have blades which are somewhat leathery and egg-shaped, shiny dark green above and paler on the underside, dotted with many glands. The inflorescence is a spike that is found directly opposite the leaves. Fifty to 150 small flowers can be found along the spike axis. The fruit is a round drupe 4 to 6 mm in diameter. It turns from green to red when ripe.

Uses:

Pepper gets its distinctive pungency from piperine ($C_{17}H_{19}O_3N$), and the aroma is derived from its essential oil, which is made up mainly of monoterpene and sesquiterpene hydrocarbons. Pepper as a spice was already used as far back as the 12th century, with Rome and Europe as the main importers. Surprisingly, there is a lack of traditional use of pepper in Southeast Asia. The increase in the use of pepper in the region is attributed to industrial development and expanding tourism.

Storage:

Pepper, ground or whole, is best stored in an airtight container in a cool, dry place to seal in the pungency and aroma that is derived from the volatile oils.

In Thai Dishes:

Black pepper is rarely used in Thai cooking. White pepper is usually used as a seasoning and fresh green peppercorns (the unripe fruit) are used as a garnish in curries or stir-fries. Green peppercorns are prized by the Thais for their crunchy texture, fiery flavour and vibrant green colour. One dish that uses these characteristics of pepper well is the *nahm phrik phrik thai orn* (green peppercorn relish), which goes well with rice, grilled or fried fish and raw vegetables. The key ingredients in this relish are green peppercorns, pork belly and shredded sour fruits.

Curry, Sauces and Relishes
chu-chi paste (a dry and spicy curry paste for frying fish)

gaeng muu phrik thai orn (pork and green peppercorn curry)
khao tang nar tang (rice crackers with minced prawn and pork sauce)
nahm phrik phrik thai orn (green peppercorn relish)

Soups
gaeng liang pla (fish and vegetable curry with white pepper and basil)
nahm gaeng chud (soup or stock)
pet ton hom (duck and spring onion soup)

Other Dishes
pla meuk thod krathiam phrik (deep-fried squid with garlic and black pepper)

NOTES

Black peppercorns are prepared by picking fruit spikes that have more or less reached full size but whose fruits are still green. These are then allowed to ferment overnight after which they are dried in the sun. To prepare white pepper, the spikes of fruits are harvested when a few fruits have turned red or yellow; these are then crushed lightly and soaked in water for 7 to 10 days. The fruits are then separated from the spike and fruit walls and left to dry in the sun where the white colour develops. There are more than 75 cultivars of pepper in India (the country of origin), 18 in Sarawak (Malaysia) and 40 in Indonesia. They are bred specifically for disease-resistance, fruit yield and subtle differences in flavour and pungency.

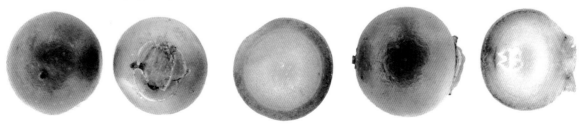

top, bottom, cross-sectional, side and longitudinal-sectional views of green peppercorns

close-up of dried buds

bark of tree trunk

Clove

Scientific or botanical name:
Syzygium aromaticum

Synonyms:
Carophyllus aromaticus, Eugenia aromatica, Eugenia caryophyllus

Scientific or botanical name of family:
Myrtaceae

Common names:
English: clove, cloves, clove tree
Thai: *kan phu* (general)

Common family name:
guava family

ripe fruits

Botanical Description:

This is a slender, evergreen tree that grows up to 20 m tall. Leaves are opposite and simple, and the leaf blade is obovate-oblong to elliptical, leathery, shiny and yellowish green above while lighter on the underside. The inflorescence is terminal with up to 20 flowers borne in groups of three along a 5-cm-long panicle. The cloves that are available commercially are the unopened flower buds, which are about 1 to 2 cm long. The bud consists of a tubular calyx and the knob of unopened petals. The flowers open to reveal numerous stamens as is characteristic of the family. The calyx and petals are tinged red. The plants flower profusely. The fruit (called mother of cloves) is oblong and fleshy, crowned with four remnant fleshy clayx lobes and a stout style. The fruit ripens from yellow to dark red and is single-seeded.

Uses:

It has been highly valued as a spice by the Chinese since ancient times. The Chinese also consider it to be an aphrodisiac. In Southeast Asia, the clove was used more as a traditional medicine in suppressing toothaches and halitosis. Cloves were also used as a stimulant and carminative. In Java, the fruits were given to women after confinement and girls about to get married in the belief that it contracts the vagina. In India, the clove has been used since ancient times to fasten the betel quid.

Most of the cloves produced are used in the manufacture of *kretek* cigarettes, made from a mixture of tobacco and cloves. *Kretek* cigarettes are smoked mainly in Indonesia.

The essential oil determines the quality of the clove. The clove tree produces three different types of essential oils. Eugenol (80 to 95%) is extracted from the leaves, eugenyl acetate (1 to 5%) from the flower stems and β-caryophyllene (5 to 12%) from the leaves. Eugenol can be produced synthetically or obtained from cinnamon leaf oil. These are used as substitutes when the price of clove oil is high. The oils are used in the perfume and flavouring industries. Clove oil is also a potent bactericide and nematicide. Eugenol is used in dentistry where it is mixed with zinc oxide to make temporary fillings for cavities.

Storage:

This spice, as with most others with volatile oils, should be kept in a tightly sealed container in a cool, dry place to prevent evaporation and loss of the aromatic flavour, phenol eugenol in this case, that so characterises the clove.

In Thai Dishes:

The perfume of the clove is thought to balance the richness of curries. It should be used sparingly. For the best results, use whole cloves instead of the powder. The cloves are used mainly in the *mussaman* (Muslim) curries.

Dishes

daeng gwa dong (pickled cucumber)
gaeng hang lae (northern pork curry)
gaeng mussaman (Muslim curry)
khao buri ('city' rice)
khao soy (curry noodles from the Tai people,
an ethnic group living in southern China,
parts of Indochina and South Asia)
mus-yao than (stuffed trout)

NOTES

This spice has had a long history and is mentioned in Chinese writings dating back to the Han Dynasty in the third century B.C. Not only was it an essential component in the famous Chinese 'five-spice' powder used in cooking, it was also used as a deodorant. In addition, anyone speaking to the emperor had to chew on cloves beforehand to prevent bad breath! The clove trade is steeped in war and intrigue and is one of the most important crops to influence world history. Native to the Moluccas (islands of eastern Indonesia, once known as the Spice Islands.), the clove is also an important ingredient in the famous Worcestershire Sauce.

sapling showing the characteristic conical crown

side view of intact fruit   *fruit with fruit wall removed to show the pulp surrounding the seeds*   *seeds removed from the pulp*

tamarind tree topiary at the Grand Palace, Bangkok

Tamarind

Scientific or botanical name:
Tamarindus indica

Synonyms: Nil

Scientific or botanical name of family:
Caesalpiniaceae

Common names:
English: Indian date, sweet tamarind, tamarind
Thai: *bakham somkham*, *makham*, *makham wan* (general), *bakham* (northern Thailand), *somkham* (Peninsular Thailand)

Common family name:
peacock flower family

flowers and buds

leafy branches bearing fruits and flowerrs

Botanical Description:

Up to 25 m tall, this tree is moderately deciduous because it favours a monsoonal climate. The crown is densely round and supported by much branching. The leaves are simply pinnate with small, oblong and oppositely arranged leaflets. The flowers are pretty and arranged on a short inflorescence 5 to 8 cm long. There are four sepals that are reddish on the outside and yellow inside. Only three petals develop fully, two spreading laterally like wings and one as a keel in the centre. The petals are pale yellow with deeply pink to red veins. The legume is about 5 to 15 cm long and is sausage-shaped, velvety brown and constricted between the seeds. The pulp that surrounds the seeds is light brown to red and has an extremely sour yet sweetish taste.

Uses:

The pulp contains tartaric acid in extremely high quantities (8 to 14%) and sugars (up to 40%). It is used in chutneys and sauces.

Almost all parts of the plant are useful and are either edible or used in folk medicine. An oil-like liquid extracted from the pulp is a formal entry in many pharmacopoeias for its use as a refrigerant and laxative. The flowers and leaves are eaten in curries or as vegetables. The bark can be used as a masticatory and has astringent properties. The starchy seed is also edible and is used for feeding ruminants or crushed and boiled to make a roofing material paste. Besides its culinary and medicinal applications, the pulp is also said to be an excellent cleaning agent for metals. The wood can be used as fuel and makes excellent timber.

Storage:

Tamarind pulp is sold in brown blocks wrapped in cellophane or in polythene. It is best kept in the refrigerator in the plastic wrap. In doing so, it will keep for close to a year.

In Thai Dishes:

Tamarind water is one of the main souring agents in Thai cuisine. The water is prepared by soaking the pulp of the tamarind in water and straining it to get rid of the fibre and seeds. Tamarind and sugar are the main seasoning in *gaeng mussaman*, distinctive curries which are thought to be a Persian introduction to Siam sometime in the 16th century. The young leaves are also used in Thai soups.

Curries and Sauces
gaeng mussaman gai (Muslim curry with chicken)
gaeng phet taet (hot and sour prawn
and cucumber curry)
nahm phrik paw (roasted chilli paste)
nahm pla wan (sweet fish sauce)
pla jian (fish with ginger sauce)
peanut sauce for *satay* (Thai recipe)

Soups
gaeng jeut dork makham (tamarind leaf soup)
gaeng tom sum (sour pork and vegetable soup)

NOTES

This seems to be yet another plant species rescued by cultivation as its origins are uncertain. The Greek philosopher Theophrastus (371–286 B.C.), the immediate successor of Aristotle and a botanist of antiquity, was familiar with the tamarind, proving that this plant has long been a cultivated tree.

The Arabs and Persians, depending on the colour of the pulp, called the tree the Indian date (*tamar hindi* and *tamar i hindi,* respectively). This became the source of the word 'tamarind'.

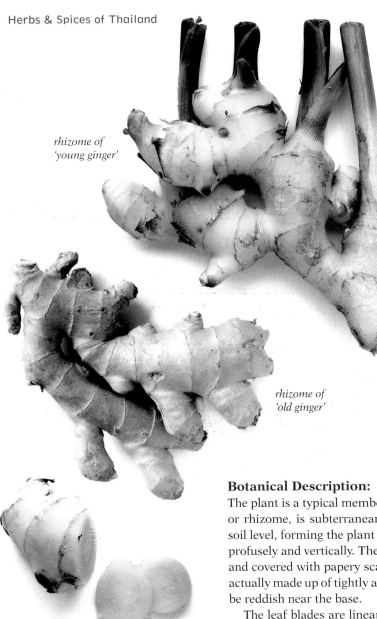

rhizome of 'young ginger'

rhizome of 'old ginger'

cross-sections of rhizome of 'young ginger'

Ginger

Scientific or botanical name:
Zingiber officinale

Synonym:
Amomum zingiber

Scientific or botanical name of family:
Zingiberaceae

Common names:
English: ginger, Canton ginger, common ginger, culinary ginger, green ginger, stem ginger
Thai: *khing*, *khing-daeng*, *khing klaeng* (general), *khing phueak* (Chiang Mai)

Common family name:
ginger family

Botanical Description:

The plant is a typical member of the ginger family. The stubby, fleshy stem, or rhizome, is subterranean and grows horizontally at or just below the soil level, forming the plant part that is used as the spice. It branches quite profusely and vertically. The surface of the ginger stem is yellow to reddish and covered with papery scales. The pseudostems found above ground are actually made up of tightly arranged leaf sheaths and are pale green but may be reddish near the base.

The leaf blades are linear to lanceolate, up to 30 cm long by 2 cm wide and finely parallel-veined. The inflorescence is a scape, which means that it is a naked flowering stem with some scale leaves, arising from an underground stem. It resembles a flaming torch and is 15 to 30 cm long. Broad scales of the flower bracts tightly overlap and cover the upper part

96

of the inflorescence. From within the scales emerge fragile-looking tubular flowers that are pale yellow and widen into three somewhat equal lobes. The most striking part of the flower is the lip, which is almost circular and tapers to the base into a 3 to 4 mm long tube. The lip is dark purple with blotches of pale yellow inside. Although resembling a petal in all respects, the lip is not a true petal but is formed by two to three modified stamens.

Uses:

Ginger is a widely used spice and the three main products are fresh (green) ginger, dried whole or powdered ginger and preserved ginger. Fresh ginger can be made into ginger ale and is used as a flavouring in Southeast Asia, cooked and taken as a vegetable or eaten raw. Ground, dried ginger is used worldwide in cooking and in flavouring confectionery or processed foods. Preserved ginger is used in jams and cakes.

Essential oil and ginger oleoresin are the two main components that give ginger its characteristic aroma and flavour. The oleoresin gives ginger its pungency, with the pungent principles being gingerols and shogoals, which are actually the plant's non-volatile phenols.

There has been a long history of the medicinal use of ginger in China and India. It is used against a wide range of ailments including boils, chest congestion, colds, coughs, diarrhoea, dysentery and other gastro-intestinal problems, fever, itchiness, migraine, nausea and a whole host of other problems. It can be made into a lotion and rubbed onto the body after childbirth or applied to swellings, used against rheumatism or in baths to combat fever.

Storage:

Ginger, especially young ones, should be loosely wrapped in a dry paper towel to absorb excess moisture and stored in the refrigerator's vegetable crisper. When kept this way, the ginger should last more than a week. Rhizomes also tend to dry out quickly so wrapping them helps to prevent excessive desiccation. Even when dried, these can be used in making soup stocks. 'Old ginger', where the outer layer or periderm is better developed to tolerate more drying conditions, can be kept in the open in a cool, dry place.

In Thai Dishes:

Ginger is used mainly to counter pungent meat and poultry smells and to remove strong fishy odours in seafood.

Curries and Pastes
panaeng gai (chicken in thick red sauce)
phrik gaeng (curry pastes, including the *gaeng panaeng*, or Thai Penang curry; *gaeng keo wan*, or Thai green curry; and *gaeng phet daeng*, or Thai red curry)

Seafood Dishes
bpu tarlae neung (steamed crab)
pla jian (fish with ginger sauce)
pla neung khing (steamed fish with ginger)
tom kem pla insri (braised mackerel)

Soups
nahm gaeng chud (soup or stock)
tom som hoi malaeng puu (mussel and ginger sour soup)

Other Dishes
khao buri ('city' rice)
khing dong (pickled ginger)

NOTES

The ginger derives its name from the Sanskrit name *singabera*. It has a very long history of cultivation and is believed to have been introduced to the Greeks and Romans no later than the first century A.D.

Recipes >>>

Laab Gai (Northeastern Chicken Salad)

A light and refreshing salad that can be served as part of a main meal or as an appetiser

Ingredients

Bird peppers	10, coarsely pounded
Roasted chilli paste (*nam phrik paw*)*	2 Tbsp
Fish sauce	2 Tbsp
Palm sugar (jaggery)	1 Tbsp, crushed, or brown sugar
Lemon or lime juice	3 Tbsp
Coconut milk	60 ml
Chicken breast	250 g, boiled for 10 minutes or until tender, then sliced
Lemon grass	6 stalks, finely sliced
Kaffir lime leaves	4, finely sliced
Coriander leaves	50 g, finely sliced
Mint leaves	100 g, finely sliced

Garnishing

Lettuce leaves	10 pieces
Tomatoes	2, cut into wedges
Red chillies	3, seeded and cut into strips
Cucumber	1, cut in half and finely sliced
Radish	1, peeled and sliced

Method

1. Blend (process) bird peppers, roasted chilli paste, fish sauce, palm or brown sugar, lemon or lime juice and coconut milk into a salty-sour dressing.
2. Mix chicken with lemon grass, kaffir lime leaves, coriander leaves and mint.
3. Add dressing bit by bit to ensure that it is well mixed. Serve on a dish lined with lettuce leaves.
4. Garnish with tomatoes, red chilli strips, mint leaves, cucumber and radish.

*Roasted chilli paste (*nam phrik paw*)

Ingredients

Cooking oil	750 ml
Shallots	280 g, peeled and sliced
Garlic	280 g, peeled and sliced
Dried prawn	280 g, soaked and drained
Dried prawn paste	2.5-cm piece, roasted and crushed
Dried chillies	170 g/6 oz, seeded, soaked and drained
Palm sugar (jaggery)	140 g, crushed, or brown sugar
Fish sauce	60 ml
Tamarind juice	60 ml from 2 Tbsp tamarind pulp and 60 ml water
Salt	2 tsp

Method

1. Heat oil and fry shallots and garlic until golden brown. Remove and drain.
2. In the same oil, fry dried prawns, prawn paste and chillies for 3 minutes until golden brown. Cool the oil.
3. Combine fried ingredients and palm or brown sugar and pound into fine paste.
4. Add fish sauce, tamarind juice, salt and cooled oil. Blend to get a fine paste. Store in an airtight container and use as needed.

Som Tam (Spicy Papaya Salad)

The sourness of the raw papaya makes this salad an ideal way to cleanse the palate
and excite the taste buds before or during a meal

Ingredients

Raw papaya	4–5 cups, peeled and coarsely grated
Garlic	3 cloves, peeled and chopped
Bird peppers	3, chopped
Fish sauce	1 Tbsp
Lemon juice	2 Tbsp
Peanuts	2 Tbsp, crushed
Ground white pepper	to taste
Lettuce and cabbage leaves	5 to 6 pieces

Garnishing

Tomatoes	3, thinly sliced

Method

1. Julienne (or slice into strips the thickness of matchsticks) the papaya using a hand-held grater.
2. Crush the peanuts with a mortar and pestle or in a sealed plastic bag with a roller.
3. Mix the julienned papaya with garlic, bird peppers, fish sauce, lemon juice and peanuts. Toss the salad with tongs to mix well.
4. Serve on a bed of lettuce and cabbage leaves. Garnish with tomato slices.

Gai Hor Bai-toey (Deep-fried Marinated Chicken in Screwpine)

The screwpine leaves give additional fragrance and add a unique
touch to this delightful dish

Ingredients

Chicken fillet	500 g, cut into small pieces
Sugar	1 Tbsp
Sesame oil	1 Tbsp
Fish sauce	2 Tbsp
Dark soy sauce	1 Tbsp
Screwpine leaves	15
Cooking oil for deep-frying	500 ml

Paste

Garlic	4 cloves, peeled
Ground white pepper	1 Tbsp
Coriander	3 sprigs, chopped
Shallots	4, peeled
Lemon grass	1 stalk, thinly sliced
Preserved soy beans	1 Tbsp

Method

1. Combine paste ingredients and blend until fine. (Chopping the coriander releases the full flavour of the herb.)

2. Mix the finely ground paste well into the chicken pieces so the flavour goes well into the meat. Add sugar, sesame oil, fish sauce, and dark soy sauce and marinate for 30 minutes.

3. Wrap marinated chicken in screwpine leaves. Fold a screwpine leaf to create a cone. Place the chicken inside and tuck the ends of the leaf in through the cone to create a tight parcel. Trim off excess leaf.

4. Deep-fry wrapped chicken for 10–12 minutes or until screwpine leaves turn dark green.

5. Remove from oil and drain. Allow guests to unwrap the chicken on their own.

Thod mun pla (Deep-fried Fish Cake)

A light and tasty deep-fried fish cake of minced fish and red curry paste

Ingredients

Red curry paste*	140 g
Red snapper fillet	500 g, minced (ground)
Egg	1 (small)
Fish sauce (*nahm pla*)	3 Tbsp
Coriander leaves	1 sprig, chopped
Palm sugar (jaggery)	1 Tbsp, crushed, or brown sugar
Long beans	80 g, diagonally and thinly sliced
Cooking oil	750 ml
Special chilli sauce †	

Method

1. Combine red curry paste and fish with egg, fish sauce, coriander leaves, palm or brown sugar and long beans. Mix the ingredients until they are well-combined and knead into soft dough.

2. Shape 2 Tbsp of dough into a ball and flatten slightly. Press the dough into a neat pattie so that it holds together well and does not break when fried.

3. Deep-fry fish cakes until golden brown. Drain. Serve with special chilli sauce.

---

* Red curry paste

Ingredients

Cumin seeds	2 tsp
Coriander seeds	1 tsp
Dried chillies	8, soaked, drained and coarsely chopped
Kaffir lime rind	0.5 tsp, finely chopped
Salt	1 tsp
Lemon grass	1 tsp, finely chopped
Garlic	1 Tbsp, peeled and chopped
Galangal	1 Tbsp, peeled and chopped
Prawn paste (*kapee*)	1 Tbsp

Method

1. Place cumin and coriander seeds in a pan without adding any oil. Deep-fry over medium heat for 1–2 minutes until they are slightly browned and aromatic.

2. Combine all the ingredients and pound into a paste. Keep in airtight jar in the refrigerator and use as needed.

† Special chilli sauce

Ingredients

Sugar	200 g
Salt	2 tsp
Vinegar	125 ml
Water	2 Tbsp
Garlic	5 cloves, peeled and finely ground
Red chillies	2, finely ground
Shallots	3, peeled and sliced
Cucumber	1, quartered lengthways and thinly sliced
Roasted peanuts	3 Tbsp, pounded

Method

1. Boil sugar, salt, vinegar and water until sugar is dissolved.

2. Add garlic, red chillies, shallots, cucumber slices, peanuts and mix well.

Tom Yum Talay
(Spicy Seafood Soup)

A clear soup with long beans, cauliflower, turnip, carrot,
pickled mustard, catfish, prawns and squid

Ingredients

Tamarind pulp	140 g
Water	1.4 litres
Catfish	1, about 280 g, deboned and sliced into 5-cm lengths
Long beans	110 g, cut into 2.5-cm lengths
Cauliflower florets	110 g
Turnip	110 g, peeled and cut into 0.5-cm thick slices
Carrot	55 g, peeled and cut into 0.5-cm thick slices
Pickled mustard	110 g, cut into 1.5-cm pieces
Palm sugar (jaggery)	2 Tbsp, crushed, or brown sugar
Fish sauce	90 ml
Prawn	280 g, shelled and deveined
Squid	110 g, cleaned and cut into rings

Paste

Dried chillies	8, seeded, soaked in hot water and drained
Shallots	6, peeled
Dried prawn	2.5-cm square paste
Garlic	5 cloves, peeled

Garnishing

Spring onion	1, finely chopped

Method

1. Combine tamarind pulp and 90 ml water. Strain and extract juice. Set aside.

2. Combine paste ingredients and blend (process) until fine.

3. Boil remaining water, add finely ground paste and catfish and continue to boil for 5–10 minutes.

4. Remove catfish and set aside to cool. When cooled, shred and return to soup.

5. While the soup is boiling, add long beans, cauliflower, turnip, carrot, pickled mustard, palm or brown sugar, fish sauce, prawns, squid and tamarind juice. Boil for 5–8 minutes until the vegetables are tender. Garnish with spring onion.

Khao Phat Supparot (Fried Rice with Prawn, Chicken and Pineapple)

A dish of stir-fried rice sweetened with pineapple cubes and made complete
with chicken and chicken sausage

Ingredients

Thai fragrant rice	375 g, washed and drained
Water	625 ml
Ripe pineapple	1, about 1.5 kg
Cooking oil	3 Tbsp
Shallots	10, peeled and sliced
Dried prawns	85 g, soaked in hot water for 5 minutes, drained and chopped
Chicken breast	280 g, cut into small cubes
Chicken sausages	4, cut into small cubes
Fish sauce	3 Tbsp
Meat curry powder (optional)	2 Tbsp
Light soy sauce	60 ml
Sugar	1.5 Tbsp

Garnishing

Lettuce leaves	5 to 6 pieces
Coriander leaves	55 g, chopped
Red chilli	1, cut into small strips and soaked in cold water

Method

1. Combine rice and water and cook. Fluff rice and set aside to cool.

2. Cut pineapple in half lengthways. Run a knife around the edge of pineapple, cut and scoop out flesh. A small sharp knife will allow better control when carving. Cut flesh into 1-cm cubes to get 1 cupful. Put shell (casing) aside.

3. Heat cooking oil and fry shallots until brown and crisp. Set aside. In the same oil, sauté dried prawns until fragrant. Add chicken and sausage cubes and fry until chicken is cooked. Be sure to cook the chicken in hot oil to seal in the juices while retaining the tenderness.

4. Add fish sauce, meat curry powder (optional), soy sauce, sugar and cooked rice. Mix well. Add pineapple cubes and fry for 2–3 minutes. Note: add the pineapple cubes at the final stage so as not to overcook them. Set aside.

5. Heat pineapple shell (casing) in a 180°C preheated oven for 10 minutes. Remove from oven and fill with pineapple fried rice.

6. Garnish rice with lettuce, crisp-fried shallots, coriander leaves and chilli strips.

Glossary >>>

1,8-cineole — A liquid, $C_{10}H_{18}O$, with a camphor odour contained in many essential oils (as of eucalyptus) and used especially as an expectorant and flavouring agent. Also called eucalyptol.

A abortifacient — A drug or other chemical agent that causes abortion

alcohol — A group of hydrocarbon compounds, such as common alcohol (ethyl alcohol, ethanol) that is found in beer, wine or spirits, in which a hydroxyl group (-OH) substitutes for an atom of hydrogen (H)

aldehyde — A colourless, mobile and very volatile liquid obtained from alcohol by certain processes of oxidation. The aldehydes are intermediate between the alcohols and acids and differ from the alcohols by having two fewer hydrogen atoms in the molecule. They are highly reactive chemical compounds and are used in making resins, dyes and organic acids. See *alkanal*.

alga (plural 'algae') — This is a primitive chlorophyll that contains mainly aquatic, eukaryotic organisms which lack true stems, roots and leaves, including phytoplankton, seaweeds and stoneworts.

aliphatic — Of the open-chain class of organic or methane-derivative compounds

alkaloid — Any member of a class of over 3,000 known nitrogen-containing compounds (such as caffeine, cocaine, morphine and nicotine) that is typically basic (pH over 7) and is produced by plants. These have strong physiological effects on animals (including humans) and are synthesised from amino acid precursors such as tryptophan and tyrosine.

alkanal — A chemical belonging to the class of organic compounds called aldehydes. Alkanals have the carbonyl group at the end of the saturated carbon chain and have the functional group -CHO.

alkenal — A chemical that is the decayed product of an unsaturated fatty acid in plants

allyl-sulphide — Any one of the sulphur-containing phytochemicals of the *Allium* species (such as garlic, onions and leeks) and is responsible for the pungency in garlic.

alternate leaves — The condition in which the stem bears one leaf per node

anaesthetic — A drug that causes temporary loss of bodily sensations and produces insensibility to pain

analogous — Corresponding to something else; bearing some resemblance or proportion

anethole — Also known as anethol, aniseed camphor or oil of aniseed, it has the formula $C_{10}H_{12}O$. It is used commercially for flavouring and perfumery. See *trans-anethole*.

angiosperm — A flowering plant. Angiosperms produce seeds that are usually fully enclosed by a fruit which develops from a flower.

annual — A plant that completes its life cycle, i.e., from flowering to seed production to death of vegetative parts, within a single growing season. Compare *biennial*, *perennial*.

anther — Terminal part of a stamen that contains the pollen-containing pollen sacs

antibacterial — Pertaining to or any substance used to kill bacteria like an antibiotic

antibilious — Of use to remove excess bile and can thus aid in cases of biliary and jaundice conditions

anticatarrhal — Something that is efficacious against catarrh, the inflammation of the nose and throat, through increasing discharge of fluid from the mucous membranes

anticholeric — Pertaining to or any substance acting against irritation

antifungal — Pertaining to or any substance used to kill fungi like an antibiotic kills bacteria

antiprotozoal — Pertaining to or any substance used to fight diseases, including malaria, that are caused by protozoa (unicellular, animal-like organisms)

antipyretic — Pertaining to or any substance used to bring down fevers

antiseptic — Pertaining to or any substance that prevents or retards the growth of bacteria. Alcohol is a common antiseptic.

antispasmodic — Pertaining to or any substance used to alleviate sustained, often painful, contractions of the muscles

antitumour — Pertaining to or any substance that kills tumours or malignant growths

apex (plural 'apices' or 'apexes') — Tip or topmost part. In a shoot or root, this tip contains the apical meristem which has actively-dividing cells that are precursors to vegetative or reproductive tissues.

aphrodisiac — Any agent or chemical that arouses or enhances sexual desire

appressed — Lying flat against or pressed close to the structure to which it is attached

aqueous — Similar to or containing or dissolved in water; aqueous solutions

aril — An outgrowth of the ovule (precursor of the seed). Mace, the net-like, reddish covering of the nutmeg seed is an example of an aril, as is the yellow pulpy flesh of the durian that is eaten or the flesh around the seeds of the litchi, longan or rambutan.

asexual reproduction — Reproduction without the fusion of male and female sex cells or gametes. Here, the genetic make-up of the offspring is identical to that of the parent organism.

astringent — A tannin-containing substance that contracts tissue by precipitating proteins and can thus reduce secretions and discharges

axil — Upper angle between a leaf and the stem or twig

axillary bud — Bud in the axil of the leaf

B **bactericide** — A substance that kills bacteria or inhibits their growth; a term often used to describe antibiotics

berry — A fleshy, non-splitting, usually many-seeded fruit containing no hard parts except the seeds

β-caryophyllene — A spicy-woody tasting, colourless to pale yellow oily liquid, usually extracted from cloves, amongst other spices or fruits, used in citrus flavours or spice blends, especially in chewing gum as well as in soaps and detergents

betel quid — A stimulant, used mainly in Asia, in which powdered betel nut (*Areca catechu*) is combined with tobacco, betel leaves, lime and various flavorings such as fennel seed. The quid is placed between the cheek and gum and remains there for an extended time, sometimes overnight. Betel is a mild stimulant but has recently been thought to be linked to oral cancers.

biennial — A plant that lives for two growing seasons. In the first season, food may be stored for use during flower and seed production in the second season. See *annual, perennial.*

bipinnate leaf — A leaf whose leaflets are also pinnate. Compare *pinnate.*

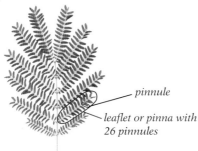

bipinnate leaf with 12 leaflets

bisexual — Bearing both sexes. A bisexual flower has both stamens and pistil(s).

bitter — A herb or spice that tastes bitter and is thought to act as a stimulating tonic for the digestive system

botanical name — The scientific name of a plant. See *scientific name.*

botanist — A scientist who studies plants

bracts — A modified leaf that subtends a flower or inflorescence in its axil

British Herbal Pharmacopoeia — A reference that provides monographs of quality standards for herbs commonly used in the preparation of botanical drugs in the United Kingdom. This is a publication of the British Herbal Medicine Association.

bulb — An underground storage organ that is made up of a highly compressed stem, almost like a disc, with roots on its lower half and above it fleshy leaf bases surrounded by protective scale leaves

bulbil — Any small, bulb-like structure usually formed in a leaf axil that can separate from the parent plant to reproduce vegetatively

bund — An embankment that prevents flooding

C calyx — A collective term for all the sepals of a flower. In plants where the sepals are fused or joined together, 'calyx' is used in place of 'sepals' to describe that part of the flower.

camphor — A tough, white, aromatic resin, or gum, obtained from different species of the Laurus family, especially from *Cinnamomum camphora.* Camphor is volatile and fragrant and is used in medicine as a diaphoretic, a stimulant or sedative.

capsule — A dry fruit, normally splitting upon ripening

carbohydrate — A generic term for molecules that have a basic empirical formula of $C_x (H_2O)_y$. They are normally classified as mono-, oligo- or polysaccharides, depending on whether they are single sugars, short-chain molecules or large polymers, respectively.

carminative — A substance rich in volatile oils and by their action stimulates the peristalsis of the digestive system and relaxes the stomach, thereby supporting digestion and preventing gas build-up in the digestive tract

capsaicinoid — Group of crystalline alkaloids that includes capsaicin ($C_{18}H_{27}NO_3$), the principle ingredient that causes the pungency or 'heat' in chillies

carpels — The unit of female reproduction in a flower. This bears the ovules which are the precursors to the seeds that develop after fertilisation.

chlorophyll — The green pigment in plants that functions in photosynthesis by absorbing radiant energy from the sun

cholera — A highly infectious and deadly disease characterised by frequent evacuation of the bowels and vomiting, caused by the bacteria *Vibrio cholerae*

chromosome — A condensed DNA-histone protein thread usually associated with RNA, occurring in the nucleus of the cell. Chromosomes contain a line of different genes.

chutney — A mixture of fruit, spices, sugar and vinegar that is eaten cold, especially with meat or cheese

cineole — 1,8-cineole, also called eucalyptol, is a major component of camphor-scented essential oils found in eucalyptus leaves, bay leaves and other aromatic plant foliage. Recent clinical research has demonstrated 1,8-cineole's effectiveness in reducing inflammation and pain and also in promoting leukemia cell death.

club moss — Also called ground pine, the common name for plants in the division Lycophyta. Club mosses are evergreen herbs with tiny, needle-like leaves and often cone-like clusters of small leaves (known as strobili), each with a kidney-shaped spore capsule at its base.

colic — Acute abdominal pain (especially in infants)

condiment — A flavour enhancer of food, particularly a sharp or strong smelling seasoning

congee (also spelt 'conjee') — Rice porridge (boiled in water)

cordial — A strong, highly flavoured sweet liquor usually drunk after a meal; a liqueur

corolla — A collective term for all the petals of a flower. See *petal*.

crossing (of plant) — Usually the outbreeding of genetically unrelated individuals. Crossing may entail the transfer of pollen of one individual to the stigma of another different genotype, usually to confer favourable traits of both individuals to the offspring.

culinary — Of, or relating to or used in cooking

cultivar — Any variety or strain of plant that has been produced horticulturally and is not normally found in the wild. Cultivar is the shortened form for 'cultivated variety'.

cultivated variety — See *cultivar*

cup — Approximately 240 ml (in recipes)

curcumin — A mixture of compounds derived from turmeric

curry — A kind of stew cooked with curry powder, a highly spiced mixture from South or Southeast Asia

D **d-borneol** — A rare variety of camphor, resembling ordinary camphor, from which it can be produced by reduction

decoction — Extraction by boiling of water-soluble drug substances. When the plant or plant part is boiled in water, the strained liquor is called the decoction of the plant.

decussate — Applied to the arrangement of leaves in which each pair of leaves that arise at each node is at right angles to the pairs above and below it

desiccation — To dry completely

diarrhoea — A frequent looseness or purging of the bowels

discoid — Having a flat, circular shape; shaped like a disk

distal — The region of the organ that is furthest from the point of attachment to the main body of the plant

distillation — The act of purifying liquids through boiling, condensing steam or gaseous vapours to a pure liquid. Pollutants and contaminants may remain in a concentrated residue.

diuretic — Any substance that tends to increase the flow of urine

d-pinene — Pinene is widely distributed in volatile oils, d-pinene being the principal constituent of American oil of turpentine

dropsy — Swelling from excessive accumulation of blood serum in tissue

drupe — Fleshy indehiscent fruit with usually a single seed that is covered with the bony or tough inner layer of the fruit fall, for example, the fruit of almonds, cherries, jujubes, peaches, plums and olives; synonymous with stone fruit

dysentery — An infection of the intestines marked by severe diarrhoea

dyspepsia — A disorder of the digestive function characterised by discomfort, heartburn or nausea; synonymous with indigestion or upset stomach

E **eczema** — An inflammatory disease of the skin, characterised by the presence of redness and itching, eruption of small vesicles and the discharge of a watery exudation, which often dries up, leaving the skin covered with crusts.

elemicin — The chemical 5-allyl-1,2,3-trimethoxybenzene, $C_{12}H_{16}O_3$, present in nutmeg

ellipsoid — A surface whose plane sections are all ellipses or circles

embrocation — A medicinal liquid mixture that is rubbed into the skin to relieve muscular stiffness and pain emmenagogue — Any substance that promotes menstrual discharge

endorphin — A natural morphine-like substance that reduces pain and gives a feeling of well-being, also produced by exercise or exposure to sunlight

essential oil — One of the volatile oils having the odour or flavour of the plant from which it comes; used in perfume and flavouring

ether — Any of a class of organic compounds that have two hydrocarbon groups linked by an oxygen atom

ethylene — A flammable, colourless, gaseous alkene; obtained from petroleum and natural gas and used in manufacturing many other chemicals

eugenol — A phenol which is colourless aromatic liquid with the formula $C_{10}H_{12}O_2$. This is used as a painkiller in dentistry and for flavours and perfumes.

eugenyl acetate — $C_{12}H_{14}O_3$; a clear to pale yellow oily liquid that has a mild, sweet-spicy and balsamic fruity odour. Extracted from certain essential oils, especially from clove oil and cinnamon, it is slightly soluble in water and is soluble in organic solvents.

expectorant — A drug or chemical substance that induces the ejection of mucus, phlegm and other fluids from the lungs and air passages through coughing or spitting. This may refer to any cough medicine.

F follicle — A dry fruit derived from a single carpel which splits only on one side

fresh weight — The weight of a plant or plant part when it is in a fresh state and not dried up

frigerant — A substance that relieves fever or thirst; a cooling remedy that lowers body temperature; synonymous with *refrigerant*

fruit — In the strict sense, this is the ripened ovary of a plant and its contents. More loosely, it may refer to this and any other structure with which the ovary and seeds are combined.

fungicide — Any substance that kills fungi

fungistatic — Inhibiting the growth of fungi without killing them

fungus (plural 'fungi') — One of the kingdoms of life that comprises eukaryotic, non-photosynthetic organisms which have chitin in the cell walls and obtain nutrients by absorption of surrounding organic compounds

G galactogogue — Herbs that help breast-feeding mothers increase the flow of milk

garnish — Something (such as parsley) added to a dish for flavour or decoration

geraniol — A fragrant liquid unsaturated alcohol, $C_{10}H_{18}O$, that is used chiefly in perfumes and soap

geranyl acetate — Geranyl acetate, $C_{12}H_2O_2$, is a colourless liquid that imparts a sweet, fruity, rosy, somewhat green and remotely lavender-like odour of moderate tenacity. It is widely used in floral and citrus-type perfumes and in fruit flavour compositions.

gingerol — Member of a group of structurally related polyphenolic compounds isolated from ginger and known to be the active constituents

gland — Any specialised structure in or on the plant body, producing a secretion

globose — Spherical or globular

gonorrhoea — A common sexually-transmitted disease caused by the bacterium *Neisseria gonorrhoeae*; symptoms are painful urination and pain around the urethra

Gram-negative — To describe a bacterium whose cell wall stains pink (negative) in Gram stain

Gram-positive — To describe a bacterium whose cell wall stains purple (positive) in Gram stain

gripe — Spasmodic intestinal pain

H halitosis — The condition of having a stale or foul-smelling breath

hallucinogenic — A property of a drug or chemical that produces hallucinations or other bizarre aberrations in mental functioning

herb — A plant or plant part used for its medicinal, savoury or fragrant qualities

herbaceous — Referring to a small, non-woody seed-bearing plant

hoary — Grey or white with or as if with age

homonym — In formal nomenclature, an identical name for two or more taxonomic groups

hydrocarbon — Any of a class of organic chemical compounds composed only of the elements carbon and hydrogen. The carbon atoms join together to form the framework of the compound and the hydrogen atoms attach to them in many different configurations. Hydrocarbons are the principal constituents of petroleum and natural gas.

I indigestion — Digestion marked by pain

inflorescence — A flowering shoot consisting of two or more flowers inserted on an axis

K ketone — An organic compound (such as acetone) with a carbonyl group attached to two carbon atoms

L lactation — Secretion and yielding of milk by females after giving birth

lanceolate — Lance-shaped

laxative — Pertaining to or being a substance that loosens or relaxes the bowels, specifically a substance for relieving constipation

legume — Typically pod-like fruit of leguminous plants (alfalfa, beans, peas, vetch, etc.), derived from one carpel and when ripe, usually splitting on two sides

libido — Sexual drive

limonene — A colourless liquid abundant in the essential oils of pine and citrus trees. Limonene is used as a lemon-like odorant in industrial and household products and as a chemical intermediate.

linalool — A fragrant liquid alcohol, $C_{10}H_{18}O$, that occurs both free and in the form of esters in many essential oils and is used in perfumes, soaps and flavouring materials

liqueur — Flavoured and sweetened distilled liquor, with alcohol content ranging from 24 to 60% by volume

Listeria — A genus of bacterium, to which the well-known species Listeria monocytogenes belong. It can cause endocarditis (inflammation of the heart lining), septicemia (blood poisoning), skin lesions and other conditions.

lobe — A projection, usually rounded, of an organ or part, separated from another lobe by a sinus, a recess or a depression

lumbago — Rheumatic pains in the lower back and loins (lumbar region)

M mace — The spice derived from the dried aril of the nutmeg (Myristica fragrans) seed

malaria — A human disease that is caused by sporozoan parasites (genus Plasmodium) in the red blood cells, transmitted by the bite of anopheline mosquitoes, and characterised by periodic attacks of chills and fever

Malesia — The biogeographic region covering the southern-most tip of Thailand, Malaysia, Singapore, Indonesia, Brunei, the Philippines, Timor-Leste and Papua New Guinea to the Bismarck Archipelago

marinade — A spice, herb, water, liquor and/or vinegar mixture in which meat or fish is soaked or wet thoroughly before cooking to improve flavour

marinate — To wet thoroughly or soak in a marinade

masticatory — A substance chewed to increase saliva

menthol — A crystalline alcohol, $C_{10}H_{20}O$, that occurs especially in mint oils and has the odour and cooling properties of peppermint

methyl chavicol — Colourless liquid with an aniseed smell; main liquid constituent of anise oil is methyl chavicol, an isomer of anethol.

micrometre — A unit of length equal to one millionth of a metre or one thousandth of a millimetre; also called a micron

migraine — A condition in which pain affects only half of the head or face, usually accompanied by nausea

monoterpene hydrocarbon — Any of a class of terpenes, $C_{10}H_{16}$, containing two isoprene units per molecule

monoterpenoid — Also called a monoterpene that consists of two isoprene units, i.e., $(C_5H_8)_2$ or $C_{10}H_{16}$. See terpenoid.

mucilage — A water-based, viscid solution containing proteins and polysaccharides

mulch — A protective covering (of sawdust, compost or shredded paper) spread or left on the ground to reduce evaporation, maintain even soil temperature, prevent erosion, control weeds, enrich the soil or keep fruit clean (as in strawberry cultivation)

myrcene — Colourless viscous liquid with the formula $H_2C=CHC(=CH_2)CH_2CH_2CH=C(CH_3)_2$. Menthol and citronella is produced from myrcene.

myristicin — An allyl benzene is a psychotropic oil extracted from the nutmeg seed and is responsible for the odour of nutmeg.

 narcotic — Drug that produces analgesia (pain relief), narcosis (state of stupor or sleep) and addiction (physical dependence on the drug). In some people, narcotics also produce euphoria (a feeling of great elation).

nausea — Feeling of discomfort in the pit of the stomach that is associated with a revulsion for food and an expectation that vomiting will follow, as it often does

nematicide — A substance or preparation used to destroy nematodes (round worms)

neral — A structural isomer of citral that is obtained from the oxidation of nerol and is used to make perfumes and flavorings

node — A point on a stem from which a leaf or leaves extend(s)

nutlet — A small version of a nut, which is a hard-shelled dry fruit with a separable rind or shell and interior kernel

oestrogen — Any hormone that promotes oestrus (sexual heat), e.g., the hormone estrone

oestrogenic — Pertaining to oestrogen or promoting oestrus (sexual heat)

oleoresin — A natural plant product mainly consisting of essential oil and resin

ophthalmia — An inflammation of the membranes or coatings of the eye or of the eyeball

opposite leaves — The condition in which the stem bears two leaves per node

orthotropic — Growing vertically upwards. See *plagiotropic*.

ovary — The enlarged, rounded and usually basal portion of the carpel or pistil of a flower that bears the ovules (which contain the eggs) and consists of one or more carpels. See *pistil*, *style*, *stigma*.

pathogen — A specific causative agent (e.g., bacterium or virus) of disease

pedicel — The stalk of the flower

perennial — Present during all seasons of the year. Compare *annual*, *biennial*.

pericarp — Wall of the fruit

petal — In a flower, the one component of the inner floral parts, usually just inner to the sepals and surrounding the stamens. Petals are usually colourful (not green or greenish) to attract insect pollinators and are commonly found in one or more whorls. See *corolla*.

pharmacopoeia — A book describing drugs, chemicals and medicinal preparations; especially one issued by an officially recognised authority and serving as a standard

phenol — Any of one of the acidic compounds analogous to phenol in a strict sense (C_6H_5OH) and are regarded as a hydroxyl derivative of aromatic hydrocarbons

pinene — Either of two liquid isomeric unsaturated bicyclic terpene hydrocarbons, $C_{10}H_{16}$, of which one is a major constituent of wood turpentine

pinna (plural 'pinnae') — The leaflet of a pinnate leaf. See figure under *pinnate leaf*.

pinnate leaf — A leaf whose blade is similar to a feather in that there is a main axis with similar parts (leaflets) arranged on both sides of the axis

leaflet or pinna

pinnate leaf with five leaflets

pinnule — The second order leaflet of a bipinnate leaf which is a leaf such that the leaflets of the leaf are also pinnate. See figure under *bipinnate leaf*.

pistil — A single carpel or group of fused carpels usually differentiated into an ovary, style, and stigma; the female part of the flower

placenta (plural 'placentae' or 'placentas') — The portion of the ovary that bears the ovules.

placental — Of or pertaining to the placenta

plagiotropic — Horizontally growing. See *orthotropic*.

platelet — A component of the blood involved in clotting

post-partum — After childbirth

poultice — A soft, usually heated and sometimes medicated mass spread on cloth and applied to sores or other lesions

pseudostem — A false stem that is formed by the tightly overlapping bases of the leaves as seen in plants of the ginger family (Zingiberaceae)

pungency — The state of being pungent, which causes an irritating or sharp sensation. In this book, it usually refers to the sensation derived from tasting food with capsaicinoids from the *Capsicum* species (chillies or bird peppers)

purulent ophthalmia — An inflammation of the membranes or coats of the eye or of the eyeball containing, discharging or causing the production of pus

R *Ramakein* — The Thai version of the *Ramayana* is known as the *Ramakein* — the tale of Prince Rama and his wife Sita, and of the struggles between good and evil. Written some 2,000 years ago and accredited to the Indian poet Valmiki, the *Ramayana* opens with the founding of the rival cities of Ayutthaya, the capital of the gods, and Langka, the city of the demons. The epic tale revolves around the struggle between these two antagonistic forces, where the principal action focuses on the trials and tribulations of Ayutthaya's Prince Rama, the abduction of his wife Sita and the eventual defeat of Langka by Hanuman and his army of monkey warriors.

recurved — Curved backwards or inwards

refrigerant — An agent that relieves fever or thirst; a cooling remedy that lowers body temperature; synonymous with *frigerant*

rheumatic — Pertaining to rheumatism

rheumatism — Any of several pathological conditions of the muscles, tendons, joints, bones or nerves characterised by discomfort and disability

rhizome — A stem that grows like a root but horizontally at or below soil level, as seen in the gingers, members of the Zingiberaceae or ginger family

ringworm — Any one of many contagious fungal diseases of the skin in humans and domestic animals characterised by discoloured, ring-like patches covered with tiny, circular lumps in the skin filled with fluid and scales

rosette — A circular cluster of leaves that radiates from a centre at or close to the ground, as in the dandelion

S **safrole** — 3,4-methylene-dioxyallylbenzene, $C_{10}H_{10}O_2$. Non-amine precursor to 3,4-methylenedioxyamphetamine. Safrole has been declared carcinogenic by the Food and Drug Administration in the United States and human consumption is banned. Safrole causes liver cancer when given to laboratory animals in high doses for long periods of time.

s-alk(en)nyl cysteine sulphoxides — The alk(en)yl cysteine sulphoxides are the flavour precursors which, when cleaved by the enzyme alliinase, generate the characteristic odour and taste of onion

Salmonella — Any of various rod-shaped bacteria in the genus *Salmonella*, many of which are pathogenic, causing food poisoning, typhoid and paratyphoid fever in humans and other infectious diseases in domestic animals

satay — Spicy, skewered, barbecued meats served with a peanut-based spicy sauce with cucumber and onion slices; of Malay origin

scape — A leafless, inflorescence stalk arising from the ground

scientific name — Name of a biological organism based on a code of nomenclature

seasoning — An ingredient added to food to improve the taste or smell that it imparts

sedative — A substance that calms the nervous system and reduces stress and nervousness throughout the body

seed — The ripened ovule of a flowering plant, consisting typically of a seed coat, embryo (young plant) and endosperm (nutritive tissue)

sepal — In a flower, one component of the outermost floral parts, often greenish and usually found in one or more whorls. See *calyx*.

sequiterpenes — Molecules made of three Isoprenes or 15 carbon atoms, a hydrocarbon. They are slightly antiseptic, bactericidal, slightly hypotensive, calming and anti-inflammatory. They contribute to the lasting odour of the essential oil or the base note as most sequiterpenes consist of large slowly evaporating molecules and are antiseptic, calming and exhibit antihistamine action.

sessile — Lacking a stalk

sex chromosomes — A chromosome whose absence or presence is linked with the sex of the bearer and plays a role in sex determination. Sex chromosomes come in heterogametic (XY) or homogametic (XX) pairs. Many evolved plants have the heterogametic sex as the male gender.

sheath — Of leaves, the base of a blade or stalk that encloses the stem

shikimine — Shikimine is violently poisonous, belonging to the group of convulsants of which picrotoxin is the typical form

shogoals — A gingerol analogue; an aleoresin that has an aromatic ketone form and is found in volatile oils

shrub — A woody plant, usually of small stature, with a few to many more or less equal main trunks or stems. May also refer to a small tree, when the term is applied loosely

silica cell — One of two types of short cells in the epidermis of grasses

simple leaf — A leaf with a leaf blade that is undivided into leaflets

solvent extraction — An extraction process which selectively transfers one or more constituents from a substance by contacting it with a solvent in which the constituents are more soluble, and in which the first substance is not soluble. Essential oils can be extracted by using solvents such as ethanol, ether, hexane, methanol or petroleum and is often used on fragile material which would not be able to handle the heat of steam distillation.

spice — Any of the various fragrant plant products used to flavour or season food

spike — An inflorescence consisting of an axis where the flowers are all stalkless

sprue — A tropical disease that is of unknown cause and is characterised by fatty diarrhoea and malabsorption of nutrients; also called tropical sprue

stamen — Male part of a flower, consisting typically of a filament and anther which produces the pollen grains

staminode — Rudimentary and sterile stamen that produces no pollen but which may function as a nectary or petal. See *stamen*.

stigma (plural 'stigmata' or 'stigmas') — The part of the pistil on which the pollen grains germinate. See *pistil*, *ovary*, *style*.

stimulant — A medicine that increases functional activity and produces energy

stoloniferous — Referring to a stem that grows horizontally; a runner

stomachic — A medicine that strengthens the stomach

style — A usually thin extension of the ovary that supports the stigma. See *pistil*, *ovary*, *stigma*.

subterranean — Situated or operating beneath the earth's surface; underground

sudorific — A substance that promotes profuse perspiration

synonym — In the case of scientific names, it refers to any scientific name that refers to an entity (e.g., species) which already has a valid or preferred scientific name. A synonym is analogous to the alias.

systemic infection — A disease that infects naturally via one of the epithelial routes, sometimes with mild or no symptoms, but which then circulates in the blood to cause disease in one or more internal organs distant from the site of infection

T **tap root** — A large central root that grows vertically downwards

tartaric acid — Also known as white crystalline dicarboxylic acid, this is an organic acid, $C_4H_6O_6$. It occurs naturally as algol (an impure form of potassium hydrogen tartrate), which is a by-product of the fungus responsible for the fermentation of wine, giving wine some of its sharp taste, and is also found in tamarind. It is added to other foods to give an acidic taste. It is also an antioxidant.

Tbsp — Tablespoon or tablespoonful; approximately 15 ml

tempeh — A kind of fermented food product of Malay origin made from boiled soya beans (*Glycine max*) and overgrown with a fungus (*Rhizopus* species)

tepal — One of the floral parts in those flowers where there is no distinction between sepals and petals; may be green, greenish or colourful

terpenoid — Also called a terpene, being any member of a group of hydrocarbons with the formulae $(C_5H_8)_n$ (where n = 1, 2, 3, etc.); terpenes consisting of isoprene units (C_5H_8)

terpinene — An unsaturated hydrocarbon with the formula $C_{10}H_{16}$. Terpinenes are oily colourless liquids that smell like lemon and/or lime.

thrombus formation — A blood clot formed within a blood vessel and that remains attached to its place of origin

tick — Any of numerous small bloodsucking parasitic arachnids, many of which transmit fever-causing diseases, such as Rocky Mountain spotted fever and Lyme disease

tonic — A medicine that promotes a feeling of well-being and gives strength and vitality to the body

trans-anethole — $C_{10}H_{12}O$, a flavouring agent from the oil of anise; chief constituent of anise, camphor and fennel; an isomer of anethole, isomers being compounds which have the same molecular formulae but different atomic spatial arrangements

tsp — Teaspoon or teaspoonful; approximately 5 ml

tuber — A swollen, fleshy, usually underground stem of a plant, such as the potato, bearing buds from which new plant shoots arise

turgidity — State of being fully inflated by absorption of water

U umbel — Flat-topped or rounded inflorescence in which the individual flower stalks arise from the tip of the inflorescence stalk

unisexual — Bearing only sexual organs of one sex. A unisexual flowering plant bears only male or female flowers, not flowers of both sexes or bisexual flowers.

V variety — A subgrouping found within a species

vegetative — Of, relating to or functioning in processes such as growth or nutrition rather than sexual reproduction

vermicide — A substance that kills worms, especially those in the intestines

vernacular name — Name used in the native language as spoken by the people of a country, or common name

vesicle — A fluid-filled membrane-lined pouch

W whorled leaves — The condition in which the stem bears three or more leaves per node

Z zest — Small piece of the peel of a citrus fruit

zingiberene — The principal component of ginger essential oil is zingiberene, a terpene compound and volatile oil

Further Reading and References >>>

Thailand in General

Central Intelligence Agency, USA. 2005. The World Factbook: Thailand. http://www.cia.gov/cia/publications/factbook/geos/th.html
LePoer, B. L. 1987.

A Country Study: Thailand. Library of Congress, Federal Research Division. http://lcweb2.loc.gov/frd/cs/thtoc.html

Royal Thai Government. Undated. Royal Thai Government home page. http://www.thaigov.go.th/

Tourism Authority of Thailand. Undated. http://www.tourismthailand.org/

Southeast Asian Herbs and Spices

Andrews, J. 1995. *Peppers: the domesticated capsicums.* Revised ed. University of Texas Press, Austin. pp. 186.

De Guzman, C.C. and J.S. Siemonsma (eds.). 1999. *Plant resources of South-East Asia. No. 13. Spices.* Prosea, Bogor, Indonesia. pp. 400.

Oyen, L.P.A. and Nguyen Xuan Dung (eds.). 1999. *Plant resources of South-East Asia. No. 19. Essential-oil plants.* Prosea, Bogor, Indonesia. pp. 277.

Siemonsma, J.S. and K. Piluek (eds.). 1993. *Plant resources of South-East Asia. No. 8. Vegetables.* Pudoc Scientific Publishers, Wageningen. pp. 412.

Thai Recipes

EasyThaifood Recipe Collection. A–Z Index of Recipes. http://www.easy-thaifood.com/A-ZMenus/a_z.htm.

Kasma Loha-unchit. 1995–2001. Kasma Loha-unchit's Thai Recipes. http://www.thaifoodandtravel.com/recipe.html.

The Searchable Online Archive of Recipes. 354 Thai recipes. http://www.recipesource.com/ethnic/asia/thai/indexall.html.

Temple of Thai. 2001. Thai recipes. http://www.templeofthai.com/thai_recipes/thai_recipes.html.

Thai Supermarket Online. Undated. 125 Authentic Thai Recipes. http://importfood.com/recipes.html.

Thaimenu.Net. 2004. The World's No. 1 Food. http://www.thaimenu.net/.

VegWeb. 2005. Regional recipes: Thai recipes. http://vegweb.com/recipes/ethnic/index-ethnic-thai.shtml.

Index >>>

  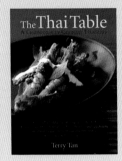 

Other Publications by **Marshall Cavendish**